PELICAN BOOKS

A862

MENTAL ILLNESS AND
SOCIAL WORK

Eugene Heimler was born in Hungary in 1922, the son of a lawyer and politician. He became aware of the dangers of National Socialism during his adolescence, and at the age of sixteen was forced to leave his local grammar school for the Jewish Gymnasium in Budapest. His first book of poems, *Eternal Dawn*, was published when he was seventeen, on the day the Second World War broke out.

During the war he was deported to Auschwitz with his wife Eva who died there. In 1947 he came to England, and after attending courses at the London School of Economics and Manchester University he qualified in 1953 as a psychiatric social worker. He organized psychiatric social work in Middlesex County Council until 1965, since when he has set up the Hounslow Project, a research into community care. In 1964 he was appointed Consultant to the World Health Organization, and spent five months as Consultant to the U.S. Government. He lectures at London University, and he sometimes appears on television. The symposium *Resistance Against Tyranny*, was recently edited by him and published in the autumn of 1966. His other books include *Night of the Mist* and *A Link in the Chain*.

In 1946 Eugene Heimler remarried, and he and his wife Livia now live in Edgware with their son and daughter. He plays tennis, enjoys travelling in Europe without a plan, and says that without his wife he would never have found life again.

EUGENE HEIMLER

MENTAL ILLNESS AND SOCIAL WORK

PENGUIN BOOKS

Penguin Books Ltd, Harmondsworth, Middlesex, England
Penguin Books Australia Ltd, Ringwood, Victoria, Australia

—

First published 1967
Reprinted 1969

—

Copyright © Eugene Heimler, 1967

—

Made and printed in Great Britain by
Richard Clay (The Chaucer Press) Ltd,
Bungay, Suffolk
Set in Monotype Baskerville

The names of patients and other details
mentioned in the case histories have been
altered sufficiently to prevent recognition.

CONTENTS

ACKNOWLEDGEMENTS

I WANT to express my thanks to Professor G. M. Carstairs of Edinburgh University for his initial encouragement: also to my friend, Mrs Elizabeth Irvine, Reader in Social Administration at the University of York, who not only read this manuscript and corrected my mistakes but also encouraged me to formulate my thoughts and ideas; her contribution towards the birth of this book is very considerable. My thanks also go to Mrs Venetia Pollock of Penguin, who has edited this book and was so very patient with me and my manuscript throughout the years. My gratitude also goes to my wife, who encouraged me to use my spare time to write and created the conditions in which writing was not only possible but enjoyable.

As a response to a letter in *New Society* three years ago I have received contributions from outstanding people and about exciting projects. I have included many of these, but, unfortunately, have had to leave out much valuable material. I want to thank everyone who contributed material for having done so, particularly Dr John Horder, Dr Alan Little, Mr Peter Hunter, Dr D. V. Martin and Miss Ann Broadhurst.

INTRODUCTION TO THE 1967 EDITION

PSYCHIATRIC community care in mental health embraces prevention, care, and after-care of the mentally ill in the community. It includes all those social and medical services that aim to help the individual and his family in rehabilitation outside hospitals or clinics. It is a rapidly developing branch of psychiatry, although it is not yet well known. This book tries to describe its scope and also, in Chapters 3 and 4, to suggest how entrance to, treatment in, and discharge from mental hospitals affect the patient and those who work for him.

Until the middle of this century psychiatry concentrated on the individual patient. Psychiatric community care takes into account his relationship with himself, his family, and with society. This fundamental shift in attitude is at the centre of this book.

When the study of psychiatry was in its infancy psychiatrists presumed that if an individual who suffered from an emotional 'cold', 'flu', or 'cancer' could have the symptoms of his illness removed, then he would be able to function better and might be able to become a useful member of society again. With this end in view the patient was taken into a mental hospital for treatment and if and when the psychiatrists felt that he was sufficiently recovered, he was returned to the community, to sink or swim as best he could. In the past discharge rates were low. Return to the community was seldom anticipated and therefore seldom prepared for. Little after-care assistance was provided.

The result more often than not was that either the patient returned quickly to hospital, or that another member of the family fell ill, or patients were kept in hospital for such long periods that they became institutionalized and afraid to face the world outside.

The idea of assisting the mentally ill on discharge from hospital is not in fact a new one. Certain small communities, such as Gheel in Belgium, have done so for a long time, and it has been tried sporadically in various places since medieval times. What is new today is the scale on which it is being applied, the attempt to enlist all the social services – both voluntary and statutory – the idea of helping the family as a whole, of trying to involve the entire community, and finally of shifting the accent from hospital to community care by Act of Parliament.

In the nineteenth century the Mental After-Care Association provided after-care hostels for patients discharged from asylums to help in their rehabilitation. Some asylum superintendents even went out of their way to see that patients had jobs to go to on discharge and advertised in the Press for suitable employment. However, little organized help was given to the patients' families who had to carry most of the burden by themselves. The effect of mental illness on marital partners, on children, on neighbours and workmates had not yet been studied, nor were services provided by the State. Charitable and voluntary organizations did some work in this respect. Relieving Officers and Duly Authorized Officers had some contact with the family, but not until this century was it fully realized that there is a definite interaction between a mental breakdown and the behaviour of the patient's family. The onus of responsibility and 'blame' was laid on the individual patient: it had not occurred to anyone that a sick person might be the product of a sick family.

The child guidance movement, which started in this country in the late 1920s, made a considerable contribution to the understanding of family psychodynamics. It soon became evident that a child's problems were very much interwoven with the problems of his mother and father and that no effective help could be given to the child if the parents themselves received no treatment.

It is in this field of family psychodynamics that psychiatric social workers have come into their own. In the beginning psychiatry was dominated entirely by medical men. Their contribution to the understanding and treatment of mental illness was, and will remain, very considerable. As time went by, however, non-medical personnel entered the field, and eventually a new profession was born: psychiatric social work. The profession (P.S.W.s) was involved with the patient and with his family and, although barely forty years old, it has already made a considerable contribution towards the care of the mentally ill and their families.

By working with a family when the first signs of mental instability occur it is sometimes possible to keep the patient at home, where he can attend an out-patient clinic or have daily or weekend treatment. If he does have to enter hospital it may only have to be for the acute stage of his illness, so that institutionalization from a long-term stay in hospital is minimized. Social workers also work with the family while one member is ill, sustaining morale, keeping the home together, helping them to face the inevitable difficulties, and preparing them for the patient's return if he is in hospital. Such a worker may also stop another member of the family from breaking down under the general strain of supporting a mentally ill person. As well as keeping the family going as a unit and preventing the spread of mental ill health, social workers see their patients in hospitals, help them when they come out, find them hostels and jobs, and see that they are helped to return to society with the minimum of friction. The patient may not be 'cured' in the medical sense but may be able to live at home with his illness. Helped and encouraged by some outstanding medical men, P.S.W.s have extended their work beyond the family to society *en masse*, to create a new awareness of mental illness and to induce the public as a whole to play their part.

The point is this: it is now possible to distinguish between clinical and social illness. A man or woman may suffer a great deal with crippling emotional problems and yet, with the help of doctors and social workers, this person may be able to function in society quite normally. In other words, he may still be ill clinically and yet be able to discharge his obligations to his family and society and to earn his living. On the other hand, someone who has no clinical symptoms at all may be quite unable to fit into society; clinically without symptoms, he may still be socially incapacitated. Psychiatric community care is less concerned with removing the symptoms of mental illness than with creating conditions,

in the family and its wider environment, to enable the
patient to live a more or less normal life with or without his
symptoms.

It is difficult to estimate the size of the problem. In trying
to assess the number of mentally ill people in the community
as a whole, I asked a general practitioner, Dr John Horder,
what he thought.

Dr Horder said: 'In general practice, psychiatry means
the understanding and management not only of psychosis,
neurosis, and mental defect but also of psychosomatic disorders, a term which is taken to mean any physical disorders
which are partly or wholly caused by emotional disturbance.
For some doctors it will also include the understanding and
management of (i) the anxieties and miseries that usually
accompany physical disease; (ii) the reaction of 'normal'
people to normal life stresses such as childbirth or bereavement.

'Numerical estimates of the psychiatric content of general
practice depend completely on definition. Estimates have
varied between 5 per cent and 75 per cent from reliable
observers in several countries. If the definition is confined
to obvious psychosis, neurosis, or mental defect a figure of
10 per cent is representative. If psychosomatic disorders are
included, the figure rises to between 20 per cent and 40 per
cent; doctors vary in their attribution of emotional causes
to various physical symptoms and disorders. (The higher
estimates of 40–75 per cent are due to the inclusion of cases
in the two categories described above.)

'A numerical statement like this does not reflect the fact
that a small number of psychiatric and psychosomatic
patients take up a disproportionate amount of the general
practitioner's time, nor that they include a high proportion
of the most intellectually complex and emotionally exacting
problems that he has to deal with.

'On average, in this country one in ten of a general
practitioner's psychiatric cases are referred to a psychiatrist.
The other nine he manages himself, some of them in collaboration with local authority and other services, but
mostly in collaboration with their relatives only.'

The same question was put to Dr Alan Little, a sociologist, who has calculated the admission rates to mental hospitals over the period 1959-60. Dr Little says that *one man in fourteen* and *one woman in nine* can expect to go into mental hospital at least *once* during their lifetime.

The problem of mental illness, however, is probably much greater than these figures indicate.

A study undertaken by a research team at the Institute of Psychiatry found that 103·6 per 1,000 persons were treated by their G.P.s for formal psychiatric illness, and a further 52·3 per 1,000 for other psychiatric associated conditions.*

The term 'mental illness' covers many states. As well as diseases such as schizophrenia, depression, hysteria, and so forth, there are episodes of minor mental illness in which people become a liability to themselves, their families, and their neighbours. They may become unable to communicate rationally, have a 'nervous breakdown', be unable to work, to support their families, look after their children, or they may become irresponsible. Some of these illnesses may not be long lasting, but they may recur, or have a disastrous effect on children or marriages if no treatment is available.

As mentioned on page 9, the public has a part to play in the rehabilitation of the mentally ill. The community cannot be said to be truly caring for its sick members if all it does is to provide a certain number of specialized professional workers to assist them and beyond that to rely on home nursing (which in some cases may undermine the mental health of other members of the patient's family, since the burden may be too heavy for them to carry alone). But here we come up against widespread hostility and prejudice towards the mentally ill, which sometimes leads people to organize protests, for instance against the establishment of a hostel for them in their neighbourhood. Miss Madeline Williams, an experienced P.S.W., discusses the reasons in a paper published in 1958:

* 'Minor Mental Illness in London: Some aspects of a General Practice Survey', by M. Shepherd, Brian Cooper, A. C. Brown, G. W. Kalton in *British Medical Journal*, 1964, 28 November, pp. 1359–63.

The community surrounds the patient with all the fears concerning violent behaviour and loss of physical control, extending these to all patients who are mentally ill, whatever their degree of disturbance. People will tell you that the images which come to their minds when thinking of mental hospitals are of patients shouting and behaving in a violent and uncontrolled way, and battles between patients and attendants. ... A visitor who had in her girlhood lived near a mental hospital said that she had a vivid mental picture of numbers of people sleeping on mattresses on the floor and of women patients all making sexual advances to the men. There are fears of indecent exposure, associations of insanity with venereal disease and masturbation, and horror of obscene language.

We see then in the phantasies of patients and of others in the community the individual who is set apart, marked, sinful, not to be associated with; the 'scapegoat' described by Sir James Frazer, the animal or human being on whom are loaded every year the evil desires and acts of the community, who is sent away or abandoned, taking the evil away from a community relieved of its sins.*

Nevertheless, the Mental Health Act of 1959 envisaged an expansion of the mental health services and the shift from hospital to community care. Its implications are that, because of the changes that have taken place in psychiatric medicine during this century, such as the introduction of powerful drugs which can control some serious symptoms of mental illness – and also because of the changes in society itself, which is more enlightened now than it used to be – a great many people will be able to receive treatment in their own homes. Most families are likely to have one member at least who is affected at some time by mental illness, even if briefly, and many people will probably come across a mentally ill person at some time in their home or at work. But home care of patients on this scale demands not only co-operation from the community but also the coordination and integration of a wide variety of specially trained social workers and social services. I hope in this book to describe the difficulties which the patients and the relatives meet. I shall show how the problem is handled by various mental

* Madeline Williams, 'Mental Illness and the Community', in *British Journal of Psychiatric Social Work*, 1958, IV, 3, pp. 4–10.

health personnel both in the prevention, treatment and after-care, and the facilities which exist for community care. I shall not discuss mental illnesses themselves in medical terms but rather the problems associated with them.

INTRODUCTION TO THE 1969 EDITION

SINCE this book was written a number of developments have taken place particularly in connection with the work described as the Hendon Experiment in Chapter Seven. Universities both in this country and abroad have been testing and using the Scale of Social Functioning experimentally and interesting results begin to emerge.

The Hounslow Project is now in a position to formulate principles, methods and theories from the variety of information coming in. Professional people who are now using the scale include the staff of two Research Centres of Social Functioning in operation, one at the University of Washington, Seattle, U.S.A. and the other at the School of Social Welfare, University of Calgary, Canada. The most important development in the understanding of social functioning has, however, occurred in our Hounslow Project, where we have now devised a further scale to measure frustration. We can now look at the relationship between satisfaction and frustration in a much more meaningful way and from this can draw certain conclusions about the nature of human problems. Furthermore, a synthesis scale has also been evolved, measuring the subjective evaluation of past, present, and future aspirations. These three scales together, the positive index, the negative index and the synthesis, form the basis of the new Scale of Social Functioning which, used in its entirety, enables us to permutate the various relationships.

The Hounslow Project, the centre from which this work had been carried out over recent years, has begun to form important links with government departments, with Industry and the Church. The practical application of our new insights is beginning to be relevant in terms of consultation, teaching, and particularly in the field of social welfare.

From modest beginnings, when scales were collected from only a few groups in the population, we now have amassed samples from many groups both in this country and abroad and we now begin to form clearer views about what normal social functioning entails. It will be remembered that the scale measures up to 100 points. It appears that those people who function normally in society score, on average, between 70–80 points. Normality, however, does not depend entirely on the satisfaction score but also on the amount of frustration. If the frustration index is relatively low and the satisfaction one moves around the 70s, then we can consider the individual as functioning adequately in society.

At any given time we are the totality of what we are and have been. The totality of our experiences is perceived by us either as satisfying or frustrating. It seems now from the work being carried out that it matters less why satisfaction and frustrations have arisen, than how these experiences are used, what for, and whether or not it is possible for the individual to find a creative way in which the frustrations can be utilized.

Frustration is the potential of satisfaction. Throughout our history, particularly over the last few thousand years, we have valued good experiences and good feelings and have tried to deny bad experiences and bad feelings. Good and positive experiences, however, are but one pole of the human situation. They are not sufficient by themselves to be creative. Experiences can only become creative if both positive and negative aspects are accepted and neither denied at the expense of the other. Yet our century does everything in its power, from pills to L.S.D., to run away from the pain of this tension and deny the 'bad', the negative. We hope to enter the Kingdom of Heaven by by-passing the entrance to Hell. We must now learn, moving towards the twenty-first century, that there is no Heaven without Hell, that it is there in the fiery furnaces of the netherworld, that the keys of Heaven are dangling from the hands of the Devil.

Throughout our history, rather than acknowledge that

Hell is centred in the heart of man, man has looked for Hell in others, projecting his 'badness' on to other groups or nations. He has spent increasing energy and ingenuity in trying to wipe out with force all the evil in this world, only to find that evil, instead of shrinking in size, appears to be increasing around us and now, at times, almost threatens us with the possibility of total annihilation.

Hell, pain, evil, 'badness', these are but a few words to describe the same thing; the inability to accept, that without the creative use of the negative, there can be no interaction with the positive pole and thus no true meaning to life can be found. The denial on the contrary has the power to build up a tension that can destroy our minds and our souls and can only find vent in a dangerous and violent society.

Polarity seems to be the nature of life on this planet. It is in the interaction of the poles that life is created. Male and female together can produce life; neither is complete without the other. In the natural sciences electricity, for example, is produced through tension and polarity. This energy is subsequently released via the two poles. It is only man's mind that has difficulty in accepting and using this concept.

We do not know what we bring with us into this world. Instincts indicate there is some kind of prior knowledge, but we do not know the extent of this knowledge, nor are we likely to know this in the foreseeable future. What we do know is that the moment of birth is only a stage in the evolution of the species and of the individual.

It seems that instincts, which we can recognize through observation, are of two kinds; those that are concerned with the maintenance of life, and those that are concerned with a threat to life.

The subjective experiencing of the life instinct is generally felt to be good; that of the threat instinct, bad. The word 'subjective' refers to both the mind and to the totality of the human organism. An embryo of ego-consciousness must be present at birth; i.e. a centre that registers that some things are happening, that there are things which are satisfying and things that are frustrating. But neither satisfaction nor frustration can exist without each other. Frustration is therefore the potential of satisfaction.

These experiences are at the most primitive pre-language level. Our words are inadequate to express this most important and original creativity. As we grow older we begin to separate the positive from the negative and this second level of experience is an attempt to try to come to terms with our human predicament. The later stage of development comes when we begin to become adult, where once more we try to combine the two aspects of satisfaction and frustration. After all, human pleasure does not lie entirely in things which are human or socially desirable. A lot of negative aspects are hidden behind our motives to do good in society.

When frustration is not given the possibility to move into creativity it does in fact cause turbulence, revolution and other forms of social disease and sickness.

We can, however, now see from the work we have done that, provided we are able to release frustrations into creativity, and not necessarily in the artistic sense, then we can bring about the new attitude to life. It may mean for the unemployed man that work is not going to be the means of expression of his creative needs but he may with the help of the educational system and other experts be enabled to find a new life task, which will give him satisfaction. The future of social work may very well be in just this area: to help people to find a new meaning to their lives through creativity rather than to provide assistance after breakdown has occurred. Those of us who work with these methods and with these measurements are confident that there is great hope for man, but this can only come about if we begin to take a completely new and critical look at those structures and systems that society has created and which are now greatly outmoded.

Hounslow, July 1968   EUGENE HEIMLER

Chapter 1

HOME CARE AND SOCIAL CASEWORK

THE PATIENT'S ORDEAL

How does it feel to be mentally ill and yet to live in the community? What are the thoughts, the feelings, of the 'patient'? How does he view himself and the world around him?

There are some experiences in life that cannot be expressed fully in words. The deeper the human emotion, the more difficult it is to find expression for it. I am constantly impressed by the difficulty mental patients have in conveying the true nature of their experiences. They sometimes burst into tears and complain bitterly that as words have been created by normal people, our language is inadequate to express their despair and isolation. A man of forty-five told me:

It's loneliness you know. Loneliness, that's it. What are words? Words can't express *that* loneliness. I was brought up in the country. Such winter nights. It was nice and warm and I can smell the bread in the oven. Then you look round in Leicester Square, and although there are hundreds of people around, you feel your loneliness even more. How far all this is from that winter night and the odour of the fresh dough. When I say it is dark and cold and I feel as if I am falling, I just say words. Miserable words. It's loneliness you have never known.

A woman of thirty-one said:

Sometimes I feel as if I want to run. Run out into the snow and the rain and the cold to find a place where I can find what I have lost. I fancy somehow there must be such *a place*. I used to go to church, but I couldn't find it there. Death is the nearest to it, I think. I somehow think that

death must be a lovely *place*. Like a dreamless dream. The
end of everything. . . .

How many of these people, who go through the un-
speakable agony of loneliness, have a companion in
pain? The nature of the experience may be such that
the sufferer cannot talk about it to relatives and friends;
he usually feels that they would be terrified if they knew
how he feels – and he is often right. Then, in turn, this
lack of human communication drives him farther and
farther into a whirlpool of desperation. How many
people do we know who are willing to listen and to
accept not only the beauty in us but also the beast? We
all rush through life with a tremendous need to communicate, yet, strangely enough, we seldom allow
others to communicate with us. So those who suffer
severe emotional pains live out their lives more or less
in a glass sphere.

A man of twenty-seven described a journey on the
London underground.

. . . You feel you are going to wet yourself . . . and *they* are
sitting there opposite and looking at you, and you think
they know it will happen any moment now. You have the
feeling that they are reading your thoughts, that they can
look into you, that they can see the hidden parts, and then
this drives you more and more crazy. It's terrible I tell you
. . . but you wouldn't understand.

These examples find in us some recognition of what
the problem might be like. There are, however, painful
experiences of another kind that seem to us so bizarre,
so much 'out of this world' that we cannot even begin
to comprehend them. The man, for example, who was
convinced that in the middle of the night his switched-
off television set was radiating some kind of rays to
keep him awake, and eventually sending him messages
from the headquarters of the Russian secret police in

Moscow that he should hang himself. Or the Hungarian refugee who managed to save his body from the revolution and lose his soul at Victoria Station, believing that the electric clock sent out rays to destroy his brain cells, so that he tried to throw himself in front of a train.

What are we to make of these experiences? As they are terrifying to an extent even to us, we may dismiss them by saying, 'These people are mad and there is nothing we can do about it.' Other people, face to face with the mentally ill, may try to convince them that no rays can come from a switched-off television set, or for that matter from the electric clock at Victoria Station. But these words of reassurance are of little help to the man or woman to whom these things are a frightening reality.

In such experiences there are two separate but interrelated processes. In the first the mentally ill hear voices or are convinced of something that is in fact untrue, and they struggle with these hallucinations and delusions. At the same time they are face to face with the second process; the people around them who disbelieve them and who naturally react with fear or mockery, which makes things even worse. Moreover, additional misunderstanding often occurs which may have serious consequences for the patient's life. This is illustrated by the following example in which a National Assistance Board officer was interviewing a hallucinated patient.

The applicant sat in front of the officer, who was trying to establish certain facts about the applicant's last employment and when he had received his last wages. At this point in the interview the applicant smiled. No doubt his inner voices were erupting into the reality of the interview and communicating something quite irrelevant. The officer saw only the smile and, as he had no 'receiving set' to pick up the voices heard by the applicant, he interpreted it as a sign that the applicant was lying about his last employment.

'What are you smiling about? Are you telling me the truth?'

The applicant no doubt once more heard the voices and smiled again. Then he muttered something to himself.

The officer was now furious. 'What did you say?' he asked angrily.

'Nothing,' said the applicant.

By this time the officer was convinced that the supercilious smiler in front of him was a liar and up to no good.

How can such a man defend himself in a world which does not understand the nature of his illness? This episode can be paralleled in many other situations of life in the community.

Some of the mentally ill may be a threat to others. A man who believes that his wife is carrying on an affair with the milkman might attack the unsuspecting milkman. Yet others, who may say strange and threatening things, would never carry out their threats. But how is one to know?

It is surprising how many people struggle with mental illness in their homes without seeking help. There are a great many people who are very severely disturbed, yet neither they themselves nor their relatives are willing to seek professional advice. Although things have changed in the past two generations, the stigma attached to mental illness still lingers.

I remember visiting a patient in North London. As he was not in, I knocked on a neighbour's door to find out his whereabouts. An elderly woman opened the door. She told me that he had been taken by ambulance to hospital just a few hours earlier with appendicitis, and invited me into her house for a cup of tea. Her son was sitting at the table and I saw after a few minutes that he was very ill indeed. He made grimaces and talked to himself. He banged the table and spat four times every now and then towards the four corners of the room. This man was in a worse state than my own patient. I asked my hostess whether she had ever asked for help for her son. She said that she had not and that not even her own doctor knew about him. *In fact, this man had never even been registered with a G.P.* The old woman kept him in the house and, as far as the National Health Service was concerned, he did not exist.

It is very difficult to assess how many mentally ill people in fact live in the community and receive no help for their illness. Possibly the above example of this woman and her son is an extreme case, but my feeling, based on some observation of acquaintances and friends, is that people do not ask for help until a serious crisis has occurred, which makes treatment and care more difficult.

CASEWORK AS A METHOD OF CARE

At present mental health departments, which exist in many boroughs and counties, are open to anyone who wishes to consult them. Anyone can walk in off the street and discuss his or her problems. However, on the whole, referrals to these new services come from doctors, hospitals, and statutory and voluntary agencies. It sometimes happens that patients recommend these departments to one another, and this enables the social workers to give immediate help. The interviews are conducted either in the patient's home or at the mental health department's offices. I found from experience that 'home visiting' was of very great value, because a number of factors came to light during these visits which were hidden in the consulting room.

If home care is undertaken for people who have never

seen a psychiatrist, nor ever been admitted to hospital, the social worker asks the patient's permission to get in touch with his family doctor. The patient usually consents but when he cannot be persuaded, nothing further can be done unless he is so ill as to require compulsory admittance to hospital under the Mental Health Act 1959 (see page 42). The general practitioner is almost invariably glad to enlist the help of the local authority's Community Care Service. The value of home care can be shown from the following example.

A mental health department's attention was called by a voluntary agency to a girl of nineteen who had not left her home unaccompanied since she was eleven years old. Whenever she attempted to do so she was overcome by a feeling of terror, felt sick – and indeed often was sick – or wet herself from anxiety. While at home she seemed perfectly happy and contented, and the casual observer might not have noticed anything strange. She was an only child of middle-aged parents, who were always arguing and fighting and had little contact with one another except for these quarrels. When the social worker first entered the house and started talking to the family, he found that whenever a question was put to the wife it was always the husband who answered; the wife just stood there terrified and unable to put in a word. The same pattern developed when a question was put to the daughter; the father answered for her too. Not only did the social worker quickly sense the undercurrent of emotional warfare in this family, but by observing the room he could detect another pattern of disunity.

The interview took place in the sitting-room, which is usually a communal meeting-place for the whole family. The girl apparently had her own room, yet this sitting-room was full of her drawings and belongings (tape-recorder, typewriter, books, and a number of her pictures hanging on the wall). In fact, this room was full of the girl and there was no evidence that anybody else lived there. As the interview continued, it became clear that everything in this family revolved around the daughter and one could see from the mother's reactions that she disapproved of this and wanted to have a place in the family for herself. Her facial expressions were described by the social worker as very revealing, like a mimic's in the old silent films. They told a story of their own without a word being heard.

After twenty minutes the social worker concluded that here were a daughter and father allied against the mother, an observation which was confirmed by subsequent happenings. Everything the father spoke about would be related to his daughter – her beauty, even her sex appeal. He even took out of his wallet photos of his daughter in a bikini and displayed them as if he were a spiv selling pornographic pictures. It was then that the real problem hit the social worker.

'Is it so abnormal,' said the father, 'for Winn not to want to leave home by herself when she has everything she wants here?' Then in a different tone, with closed fist, he went on: 'It is a dirty world out there. I don't have to tell you what goes on there, outside.'

Was it possible, the social worker thought, that this was the heart of the matter? That this man, unhappy in his marriage, had transferred all his love from his wife to his young daughter and that she was unable to break away from his demands?

'Do the twist, dear, for the gentleman.'

Like a robot, the girl got up, put on a record and started to dance. The social worker watched the parents. The father's eyes were shining like those of a man watching striptease, while the mother's face expressed disgust and great sadness. When the dance was over the social worker asked if the girl had any friends. The father replied that she had none and that she did not need any.

When, during subsequent interviews, the social worker had the opportunity to talk privately to the various members of the family, the impressions and observations of his first interview received definite confirmation. It was clear that not only was the girl sick, but each member of the family, separately, and *in their togetherness*, was ill. How could this girl receive any treatment herself with her father there to jeopardize it? If this vicious circle was to be broken, it could be done only through giving help to the whole family, possibly by various social workers taking on various partners.

Unfortunately, it was impossible to give effective treatment in this particular case because the father had not the slightest insight into the abnormality of his own behaviour. But the story shows us that when mental illness occurs, it may not always be the most disturbed member of a family who breaks down. The family is an organic unit and it is the member with the least resistance who is most likely to fall ill.

Something, however, was achieved. The girl, instead of spending her time 'enjoying' herself under her parents' close surveillance, was able to have some life of her own. She started to learn shorthand and typing, and was subsequently able to do some work, even though it had to be at home.

In other cases, however, by helping a family in their home, remarkable changes can be brought about which are beneficial to the whole family. Luckily, the problems are not always as crippling as in the case of Winn, and the family is only too eager and pleased to share its anxieties, its innermost problems, with trained outsiders. This work, however, may take a long time.

The trained psychiatric social worker during this home treatment uses the relationship between himself and his patients as his most important tool. Of course the same thing would apply if, say, two social workers took on two different members of the same family.

The use of relationship as a therapeutic tool has been the subject of many discussions and many papers. One of the pioneers of community care, Miss E. M. Goldberg, writes:

. . . In this kind of work we not only try to help our clients to unburden themselves and show them by interpretation how they have carried the past into the present; we also hope to recognize and articulate in the 'here-and-now' of the relationship between ourselves and the client, some of the client's problems in relationship, which always centre round the themes of love and hate. We help them to become aware not only of their positive feelings for us but also of their defences and unresolved hostilities in relation to ourselves. We hope to demonstrate to our clients that, although we know about some of their bad, hostile feelings, we remain unharmed by them and friendly towards our clients. This experience will often be a new and creative one for our patients and tend to lessen fears of their potential destructiveness. Whereas formerly we consciously or unconsciously tried to provoke in our clients love or positive feelings for us, by being good, friendly figures who brought out 'the good' in them, we are now trying to see also the hidden expression of their negative feelings for us and to attempt to work through them. We do this because it is likely that these negative hostile feelings form the basis of their disturbed 'interpersonal' relationships. Most of us find this endeavour to bring hostile and negative feelings out into the open very difficult indeed. For do we not all want to be loved rather than hated?*

* 'Function and Use of Relationship in Psychiatric Social Work', in *British Journal of Psychiatric Social Work*, No. 8, November 1953.

The period of care required depends on many factors. Short-term care is most likely to be effective in a crisis. A crisis in itself is not necessarily a bad thing, but for various reasons it may become a cul-de-sac. It is then that communication with another human being becomes valuable, for it may enable the patient to return to the main road. I would like to describe such a crisis which occurred to one of my patients in December 1953. She was going to get married just before Christmas, but a few days before her wedding something hit her from within the hidden channels of her mind. The case illustrates how in a short-term crisis help can be given even from an office desk.

I met Dora Haskins in my office, where she sat in front of me in an armchair. She was pale and had dark shadows under her eyes. I asked her to tell me what troubled her so much, as her doctor's note only referred to a sudden panic a few days before. I will try to reconstruct this interview, in which I learned so much about her life, fears and anxieties.

'I don't quite know where to start. I don't know what you want to know. I am very confused and afraid, but I am not sure where to start.'

Silence.

'Perhaps I should tell you what happened that night. Shall I tell you about that night?'

I nodded.

'I couldn't get off to sleep. I usually sleep like a log. I had said good-bye to Neville an hour before. You know, I was going to marry Neville.'

'How do you mean you *were* going to marry him? Aren't you going to marry him now?'

She became silent. She bit her lip and then said:

'That's the whole point, you know, I don't really know. I am not at all sure after that night.'

'Well, what happened then?'

'I'm sorry. I'm a bit mixed up. I told you I was trying to get to sleep, but I couldn't. Something kept me awake. There was a peculiar noise in the room, a sort of hissing and chirping. I don't know whether you have ever experienced this kind of noise which comes from . . .'

Silence again.

'I grew terribly restless. I felt as if the darkness and the night were sitting on me. I wanted to scream, but I couldn't even do that. It was like an orchestra coming to the end of a symphony. It was becoming a crescendo. I thought that something terrible was going to happen – that I would die or take my life, or something. I don't know what happened next, but I do know this, that I was standing in front of the lions in Trafalgar Square and the rain was pouring down. I swear I couldn't tell you if I took a taxi or if I walked, but there I was in front of the lions. I remember that because I thought that they were going to jump. Then I started to cry. I felt as if my life had come to an end. I walked and walked again, first down to the river and then to the West End. I thought of nothing else but death. . . .'

'Why death?'

'Because . . . of him. Because of Neville. We had planned this marriage for at least two years and we were looking forward to it so much. But it can't be.'

'Why not?'

'Because you see . . .' She started to weep silently. 'Because I am afraid I shall go mad like my sister Lucy. You know, two days after her wedding we had a telegram from her husband, Fred: "Lucy ill, we are returning home." He brought her back. She was crazy; she was screaming and hearing voices. She had to be taken to a mental hospital and she never came out. That's what marriage did to Lucy.'

'I see, you are afraid that if you get married you will go mad too?'

'Yes, yes, yes,' she shouted. 'I am. I have no right to happiness.'

I kept quiet. She went on:

'You know, I would be the only member of my family to

make a happy marriage because I love him so much, but I have no right to be happy.'

'Aren't your parents happy then?'

'You know what, my mother and father have slept in separate rooms since I was eight. They hate each other's guts, but they haven't had the strength to separate. I was like a blooming pawn between them. I was pushed from here to there, passing on messages, unpleasant ones, from one to another.'

'So you are convinced that you have no right to happiness.'

'I shouldn't have come here. I know I shouldn't. You don't really understand, do you? You just sit there all-knowing, but you don't know a thing. You are not at all sympathetic.'

Silence.

'I'm sorry. I shouldn't have said that, but somehow I felt that you are awful. You too. Daddy was awful to Mummy. Fred must have done something to Lucy to make her ill, and I am afraid something awful would happen to me if I got married. Can't you see?'

'I can see that you seem to think that men are devils, and that you seem to be an innocent angel.'

She glared at me angrily.

'What do you mean that I am not innocent? Just what do you mean? Now you explain straight away what you mean!'

Silence.

'It's no use your thinking that I had anything to do with Mummy and Daddy's marriage, because I didn't, you see. I am innocent.'

'I never suggested that you did.'

'Mummy and Daddy messed up their own lives, not because of me, you see.'

'I see.'

'What's the point of you saying you see when you don't see anything? You just don't understand.'

A long silence followed and, as if a curtain of darkness was slowly lifting, she put her head on her arms and wept bitterly. Afterwards, she said:

'I was a teenager when Lucy got married. I envied her, you know. She was so excited, and she always showed off. I wished her to hell.'

'You may have wished her to hell, but you did not make her mad.'

She looked at me with great surprise.

'Somehow, somehow . . . throughout these years I felt I should be punished for that. I was so angry with her happiness, and now I feel that she is hitting back at me like a boomerang.'

'It is only you that hits yourself back because you feel guilty.'

'Yes, I do, and I am very sorry, very sorry indeed. I didn't know what I was doing.'

'I know that. You were angry with yourself, angry with your parents, and, perhaps you have forgotten it, but you were wondering too whether you did come between your father and mother when you were so small.'

Fighting with her tears she went on: 'I was very fond of Daddy you know, and yet I was pleased when he was sometimes angry with Mummy. You see I have no right, no right to happiness at all.'

Since Dora was able to tell me about her fears and anxieties she became able to see her problems in some kind of perspective and to discuss them with her fiancé. This was a big step for her because she had never dared to tell him about her sister's mental illness. She brought Neville along to see me and we discussed how some of Dora's problems might have arisen and how she could tackle them with the help of her future husband.

They got married at the appointed time and subsequently had a child. Dora has had no breakdowns. She still has her problems and sometimes her feelings of guilt make her depressed, but she manages to live with her family and to bring up her little daughter.

The case-worker's function is not to undo the past. The past is done, the memories of pleasure or pain live on in the mind. The case-worker's function is to enable his patient to live his life more comfortably with himself and others – not punishing himself for the past. The case-worker is not a psychoanalyst; his methods cannot make basic personality changes, but may help to reinforce and release the healing process in his patient.

Although people in crisis can often be helped on a short-term basis, the results may not be permanent. Some residue of the past may again be activated and the patient may again need help. However, a considerable percentage of patients need only to be able to communicate at a point of crisis. Sometimes these critical moments may be very dramatic. I remember a man whose neighbour had a heart-attack. Two days later he himself produced similar symptoms. His doctor established that in fact his problems were psychological in origin, but it was still necessary to discover the reasons for his attack. When, after some discussion, he was able to see that he felt guilty because of an act of marital infidelity, and felt that he should be punished for this, he was able to establish a better relationship with his wife and also to get rid of his symptoms.

The present and the past are connected by invisible wires along which messages constantly come and go. The case-worker's function is to decode or decipher these messages and to act as a bridge between the past and the present.

The methods of long-term case work are many and sometimes rather involved. A method that may suit one patient may be quite unsuitable for another. The case-worker has got to use his skill to find the right method to suit each particular individual.

At the very beginning of my professional career I came across a young man who had been classified as 'a bloody nuisance'. He was only twenty-one, but had to be admitted into a mental hospital because of his sadistic fantasies, with which he threatened anyone who came across him. He talked incessantly about his need to cut people up with a knife, and went into gory details of how he would do this. As he did not improve, the psychiatrist in the hospital asked me to help him find some sheltered job where he and society would be safe. Inexperienced as I was, I knew that I would not be able to help this man by psychological interpretations or words of any sort, and the longer I knew him the less anxious I felt about the possibility of his ever carrying out any of his threats. He confided in me and I learnt much from being with him.

Charlie, that was his name, was more bewildered by people's reactions to his fantasies than by the fantasies themselves. I wondered whether it was possible to find him a job where he could act out some of them in reality in a socially acceptable way. I thought of getting him a job in a holiday camp as a butcher, partly because he confessed how fond he was of having a good time, and partly because I thought that being a butcher might provide an outlet for his sadistic tendencies. Eventually he got such a job and married soon afterwards. When I met Charlie a few years later, he was no longer obsessed by his disturbing fantasies. He was able to *work* a great deal out of his system.

To achieve all this took a long time and Charlie's story illustrates how, without interpreting the origin of symptoms, it was possible to enable him to live a happier life by allowing him to use his destructive fantasies in a harmless and useful way. It was only possible to help him through a relationship, but this was not based on interpretation of unconscious material. An analyst might have put him on the couch (had he been able to pay for the treatment over a period of years) and might thus have helped him to free himself from these destructive fantasies by tracing the symptoms to their sources in past experience. Whether or not this would have achieved more in the long run it is difficult to say. Had his symptoms been removed he would probably not have become a good butcher, but perhaps he would have become something just as satisfying.

Charlie had been in hospital for a short period, but it was mainly through the resources of the community that he was helped.

THE CASE OF STUART

There are other long-term cases where a patient may never go to a hospital or see a psychiatrist. The case of Stuart James is a good example of this.

Stuart was a man in his early thirties when I first met him in 1954. He suffered from a condition called 'anorexia nervosa'. The main features of this illness are considerable loss of appetite, loss of weight, and general weakness. He had been in this condition since his army days when he was stationed in the Far East following an illness which was never properly diagnosed but which confined him to a military hospital for some weeks with such a high temperature that he thought he would die. The fear of never seeing his father, relatives, and friends again, coupled with the anxiety that he would be buried in a strange land hundreds of miles from his home, filled him with horror. When his temperature subsided, he was never the same again. He looked like a living skeleton, and when I met him he seemed to me like one of those shadows from the inferno of Auschwitz.

He told me that he had been practically bed-ridden since the end of the war and that the mere effort of trying to get up and take a few steps around the room made him sweat and feel dizzy. He had given up these attempts and now all he would do was to sit on his bed for a little while. He would read a great deal and listen to serious music, but life had no purpose, no aim, and the days and weeks rolled by in grey monotony. In order to bring the outside world into his bedroom, he bought himself a telescope and would watch what went on in the houses opposite. He could also see farther afield and could pick up the movements of cars and people. His description of his 'friends', people who regularly appeared in his 'looking-glass', was dramatically tragic. He gave names to these 'friends': 'I saw Johnny again the other day. He must have a cold, because he was blowing his nose all the time'; or: 'Jill and Peter were together again. I bet it won't be long now before they get married.'

The real world, in terms of human contacts, was limited for Stuart to an elderly father and his unmarried older sister who worked during the day and looked after the family in the evenings. She couldn't get married because of her responsibilities, although there was someone who would have liked very much to marry her.

I remember clearly the first interview I had with Stuart's father, a retired high-ranking civil servant. He invited me ceremoniously into the living-room and said in his public-school voice: 'Actually, I don't quite understand why he has to stay in bed so much.' This was the greatest understatement I had ever heard. He then showed me a framed certificate hanging on the wall which testified that Stuart had passed the first part of his examination for a teacher's diploma in the pianoforte.

'Those,' the old man said, 'were the good old times before the war,' and, controlling his emotion, he added: 'He showed some promise, so I was told.'

I remember the dark paint on the walls, the darkness that sat on the rooms in the late winter afternoon, the uncanny feeling of having stepped into the nineteenth century without being able to return to the twentieth, the framed pictures of Stuart's mother, who had died when he was a little boy (he had hardly any conscious memory of her), and the portraits of aunts and uncles, some of whom had lived in mansions or country houses. Stuart, too, filled me with a sense of unreality. His words were slow and ceremonious like those of his father. Each syllable was carefully pronounced, each sentence measured to the utmost, as if he were a character in a Victorian novel.

This precision of speech, I felt, was an attempt to conceal the inner turmoil, the inner chaos. Below the surface there were gigantic whirlpools hidden in the mind.

I went to see Stuart regularly every week and in time we discussed everything under the sun. As he had considerable difficulty in talking about himself and his past, I had to let him talk about what looked superficially like 'general topics'. We talked about the infinity of space and time, and how long the light of distant planets takes to reach the earth. He was not yet aware that he was conveying to me another dimension of his problems.

'Is it not surprising,' he said once, 'that the light of a star that reaches our eyes during this age may have left the skies many, many years ago? That we can see things now that have been dead for a long time?'

In a conversational tone I answered: 'Yes, it is strange. And the opposite is also strange; that the past may be very much alive, but we feel ourselves dead to perceive it.'

In this way I gradually tried to show him how his innermost problems were expressed in the abstract content of his conversation.

About six months later he said to me: 'You seem to

think that I am psychologically ill, yet I am convinced that in fact I am suffering from a long-standing chronic physical illness. I do not believe that much is wrong with me emotionally, except *as the result* of my physical illness. If you, or anyone else, were closed in between the four walls of a bedroom, naturally you would feel depressed at times, or fed up. Don't you think?'

Of course there was some logic in this argument, provided one accepted the premise of a physical illness. But even so, he was much more than fed up or 'a little depressed'. He had already conveyed to me that he had locked up his past behind internal walls and was unwilling to break out from his self-created internment camp. This went on for about another six months and I seemed to be of little help, except in breaking the monotony of his humdrum life.

I wondered whether I was justified in carrying on, as I was doing so little good. I thought I might not be the right person to help him. But as he seemed very keen on my visits I still went regularly, though no longer expecting to be of much help. Then, quite rapidly, towards the end of the second year, a number of things happened. Stuart now spent more time out of bed than in bed, and talked increasingly about his regrets about his unfinished musical studies. Although he said he was still too weak to play the piano, he hoped one day he would be able to do so. If he only had a qualification he could have taught. Not yet, of course, *but one day perhaps*.

Now, he would say, even if he became stronger, his life would be wasted. He could never qualify, because he could not attend the Academy. I asked him if he would play the piano for me, just for a little while. Eventually he agreed, but felt very exhausted after a few minutes. The tunes he played were lifeless, lacking in emotion. Some of his old technique was still there, but he projected his gloom on to the piano keys.

Then tragedy hit the house. His father had a stroke and died, and a few weeks later his sister died as well. Now he was quite alone in the world. I was his only contact, as he put it – his only friend. The death of his family seemed to make him once more depressed. Sometimes he was on the verge of tears, but he could never cry; feelings were too dangerous for him. Yet although he had inherited a large house with tenants, and had the usual problems of income-tax, decorations, and repairs, he gradually seemed able to cope with it all. In fact, after a time, he managed quite well. Once more he was out of bed, and was dressed all day. When spring came he asked me to take him round in my car so that he would see all the places of his childhood again. Then he began to speak about the past. On odd occasions he would go down to the corner to fetch his papers, and it was on one of these little outings that the past opened up for him through an amazing coincidence. Stuart James met a married woman in this shop whose name was *Mrs James*! He knew that she was married and had children, but he could not help feeling that, in some peculiar way, she belonged to him. He spent more and more time in the shop, eventually offering to do a few hours' voluntary work, addressing envelopes and putting people's names on the newspapers. He felt happy for the first time in his life. It was a secret love, a love that did not reach his muscles. His weak body could not as yet perceive the mystery of sexual desire, but his heart was afire for Mrs James. It was then that he told me how his mother used to take him to the park. He could see across the gulf of time his mother's pale face, her brown hair blowing in the wind – the park, the games, how he fell once and hurt himself. Love had opened up the old wounds, and now Stuart was bleeding inside. He could at last feel his salty tears, and although he suffered a great deal, it did him good.

His love for Mrs James was short-lived. She soon left the shop and never knew Stuart's love for her. But now, after his first experiences of 'love', he started to reach out towards the future.

He spoke to me with great respect of a well-known piano teacher, a Mr Ralph Blane. If he was well he would ask him to give him lessons so that he could qualify at last. But Mr Blane was a very busy man, and Stuart could not yet undertake long journeys. As Mr Blane's name came up more and more in our conversations, and as Stuart was reading Mr Blane's books, I decided to ask him if he could visit Stuart. I phoned Mr Blane and he invited me to lunch. I told him about Stuart and he listened with great interest and compassion. He promised me to visit Stuart and prepare him for his final examination.

This news overwhelmed my patient. Now he was willing to practise the piano for several hours a day and, with Mr Blane's help, he eventually achieved his aim and qualified. Soon after that he started to teach pupils in his own home. He fell in love with one of them and, at the time of writing, is married.

Stuart James is not yet a completely healthy man. He still can't go out for long journeys. He still has problems, and although he has put on some weight he has still not completely recovered from his illness. But he lives a more useful and a more satisfying life.

At lunch Mr Blane had told me: 'I am not a psychologist. I am a teacher, and an artist, but I believe that if you can release the creativeness in man you have released the healing processes as well.'

R. S. Lederman sums up the situation regarding incomplete recovery as follows:

Without being able to eradicate, and sometimes even without being able to touch, the sick parts of their personality (i.e. the complexes, often deep in the unconscious, which produce symptoms) we attempt to help them to grow towards a greater awareness of themselves and their as yet undeveloped potentialities. By encouraging their positive assets we try to mobilize the natural healing powers which are inherent in everybody. By doing so we hope to start a process in which they combat the diseased parts of their psyche themselves, a fight which sometimes goes on without the conscious awareness of the patient, and often continues long after he has stopped seeing us.*

SOCIAL ISOLATION

A great many people need help on a long-term basis, although they may have no symptoms and may not be ill in either a physical or mental sense, because, essentially, they suffer loneliness. Loneliness is no respecter of age. Its problems hit many who are otherwise healthy. Some may choose to be alone, but many have loneliness thrust upon them.

Evelyn was twenty-three when she came to London to her first job, having completed her degree at one of the northern universities. Her home life was warm and loving, and she would have preferred not to come to the metropolis but her teachers advised her to do so for the sake of professional experience. At first she hoped to live in a hostel but she found that the hostels were all full. Both she and her parents were rather worried about this.

Evelyn was a tall, attractive girl and was very much in love with a young man in her home town. They decided that it was too early to think of marriage before they had both laid the foundations of their careers, which they knew would not be for at least two years. They realized that this would be a challenge to both of

* Rushi S. Ledermann, 'The Significance of Feeling in the Therapeutic Relationship', in *British Journal of Psychiatric Social Work*, No. 9, May 1954.

them as they would only be able to meet once or twice a year, but they felt that their love was strong enough to withstand this challenge and believed that the separation would bring them closer together.

Nothing in Evelyn's history suggested any abnormal development. She had loving parents, one older brother, and one younger sister with whom her relationship as the years went by had grown better and better. In short, hers was a close-knit family. She made friends easily, and excelled in science at grammar school so that her teachers advised her to study chemistry.

She found work in the research department of an internationally known firm, which involved working partly in London and partly at the laboratories near another town. Subsequently, she found herself a furnished room in this very new town where the paint was hardly dry on the houses. Although there were one or two young people around, they were either married already and had their own friends, or they were young single men with whom, for obvious reasons, she did not want to enter into close contact.

After three months of work and social isolation during the evenings and week-ends she became increasingly depressed, lost a great deal of weight, and could not eat properly. She would describe the weekends at home in her own town several hundred miles away, and the memory would bring tears to her eyes.

It was not until, on the advice of her doctor, she returned home that her depression left. No amount of case work or psychiatry could transform reality for Evelyn. No one could transplant friends and parents into her new environment. The change itself had created her loneliness and her reactive depression.

Social isolation is so common and so closely associated with mental illness that a short example of an existence that many people lead is included here. I have chosen, to contrast with Evelyn, an old lady of eighty-three with whom, some years ago, I tape-recorded a conversation in a fish-and-chip shop where we both had a meal. She was only too anxious to pour her heart out and so glad to find someone to talk to. She was a widow who had lost her husband twelve years before. At first she had stayed on in the house where she had brought up her children, but increasingly as the years went by she found that it was too much for her to manage the household chores.

She had two sons, both of whom lived outside London and could not visit her often.

It was a strange experience for me to listen to her descriptions of lonely dusks and nights. The way she spoke was almost poetic:

The summer is worse. I sit by the window and I watch people coming and going. The afternoons are longer and so much is going on in the street, and when the sun goes down I think – here comes another night.

I now live in an old-age home and at dusk everything is quiet. Most of us are looking out to see what *others* are doing. It's sort of lonely like – you know what I mean? And after supper what is there to do? To think of the old times when you were one of those who used to be out and never gave a damn for those who *looked out*. Fancy this being life. But the night is the worst. You never know whether another day comes and sometimes you don't want another day to come. You pray to God that it can be all over and then you feel miserable, because you see I am religious like.

When she died a few years later, I acquired her diary:

Monday, 2 January 1961
Not a bad day but disappointed. Nobody telephoned. Forgotten.

Tuesday, 3 January 1961
No letters from anyone . . .

Wednesday, 4 January 1961
Bob phoned today. I feel brighter now.

Thursday, 5 January 1961
Not a very nice day. Very cold, and I feel so depressed.

Sunday, 29 January 1961
Not well, in bed all day. Feeling very rotten. And so alone.
Fed up with life. Is it worth it?

Friday, 10 February 1961
Bob sent me £100, but money does not make me happy. I
am very unhappy and lonely.

Monday, 13 February 1961
Not talking to anyone. My cold is still bad. I am crying.

And so the diary continues.

The relief of social isolation is an urgent problem.
With relief, some at least of the burden of mental illness will be lifted. Only a sustained imaginative programme at a national level will be able to match the
gravity of the present position.

EMERGENCY SERVICES

As well as providing long-term services, local authorities
are also responsible for the provision of an emergency
service so that patients and their families can seek
advice or help immediately it is needed. These services
are at the moment extremely haphazard. Some local
authorities have done a great deal; others have barely
scratched the surface. To begin with, no such service
can work without skilled and trained personnel, yet
there is a serious shortage of trained workers in many
parts of the country, and even in London untrained
people are still employed.

The aim of immediate response or emergency work
would be to provide a night and day service available
to patients, relatives, and G.P.s, so that if a crisis occurs

in a family, social workers can be mobilized straight-away and can advise or take appropriate action on the spot. Although under the 1959 Mental Health Act, mental welfare officers can commit a patient to a mental hospital under an emergency procedure, emergency work is by no means always a question of removing the patient: the mere arrival of a neutral outsider, not involved in the family crisis, can often lead to an improvement in a critical situation, as can be seen in the following case.

John Law was an electrical engineer in his late forties. He was a conscientious and able man, a good father and a good husband. A few months before the crisis developed he started to have swings of mood. Sometimes without any apparent reason he became very depressed, and at other times he felt on top of the world. These alternating extremes of depression and elation went on for some weeks and the family became very worried. His doctor advised him to see a psychiatrist, who in turn admitted him to hospital for a few weeks. Various drugs were administered and he was discharged, since he was able, despite fluctuations of mood, to carry on with his work. Mrs Law, a woman in her early forties, was naturally very bewildered by her husband's sudden mood swings. She was afraid that one day he might commit suicide. At night she could not sleep, and each time he went to the bathroom she followed him on tiptoe, watching him all the time. On the night of the crisis, he became very angry because of this and locked himself in the bathroom in order to get away from her. This was not an attempt to kill himself, just an expression of anger which could happen to any ordinary couple. Fearing suicide, Mrs Law immediately telephoned her doctor, and he in turn telephoned the Mental Health Department. When the mental welfare officer arrived Mr Law came out of the bathroom and explained what had happened. In the middle of the night, over a cup of tea, the husband and wife were able to discuss their problems with the visitor, who was able to understand with them how this crisis had developed and how Mrs Law was affected by her husband's illness. There was of course no need for any further action and soon Mrs Law settled down to her normal life. While her husband's swings of mood lasted for some time, she was able not to worry about possible suicide.

Sudden admission of a patient to hospital is always a crisis for both patient and family. It is the function of social workers to explain to the relatives some of the administrative problems arising from the patient's admission to hospital, when he can be visited and what medical procedures are likely. By keeping in touch with the patient while he is in the hospital, the social worker may also be a bridge between the hospital and his home. When treatment starts the social worker is in a position to tell the relatives how the patient is responding and to prepare them generally for his eventual return home.

Chapter 2

FAMILY INVOLVEMENT

MENTAL illness can generally be divided into psychosis and neurosis. Medical opinion as to the origin of psychosis varies. Some seem to think that it may be caused by as yet unknown biochemical disturbances of the organism – possibly glandular in nature – while others maintain that it is probably psychogenic in origin. However, neurosis is generally agreed to be due to the interaction of unhealthy patterns developed in childhood with stress in the present environment. Thus, the symptoms of neurosis in the 'here and now' convey a great deal about the past.

It will probably be some time before the aetiology of these complaints is finally established. The human individual is a kind of trinity of body, mind, and environment in constant interaction. Which of these is cause and which effect we do not know. The relationship may be similar to that of a seed with the soil in which it is planted. If the seed is healthy, the earth suitable, and the climate favourable all will be well. However, variations in any one of the factors involved will affect the growth process, and each different combination of variations will produce different results. Thus a good seed in unsuitable soil may do adequately but be unable to survive a frost, whereas a poor seed in better soil may do less well and yet prove hardier against the cold. We must remember that this analogy holds good only at a superficial level. Only when we have developed a surer science of human behaviour will we know if we can carry the parallels farther.

Stresses in the family may of course express themselves through any of its members, adults or children. Whoever it is, there is increasing evidence that it is not always the most disturbed member of the family who breaks down but, more often, the one with the least resistance. Until quite recently, care of the mentally ill was directed only towards the individual who had broken down. It has now become clear that this approach may be quite inadequate, since it neglects the condition of the people around the patient, whose own tensions may have contributed to or even determined his actions. Moreover it very often happens that, if only the patient is treated, other members of the family break down as soon as the patient himself recovers.

It was the child guidance movement which first recognized that the child's and the parents' – particularly the mother's – problems were linked. The very words 'child guidance' indicated that, in its early days, this movement considered it sufficient to concentrate on the child alone. Increasingly, however, the mother was brought into the treatment situation as it became clear that her problems and the child's were connected. It is now quite common for a child to receive treatment from the psychiatrist or psychotherapist while the mother is helped by the psychiatric social worker, and treatment can even extend to the father as well. What was once a 'child guidance' service has now developed into a 'family guidance' service.

Similar patterns emerge with adult cases, although the full significance of family directed case work or psychotherapy has not yet been fully realized, nor is there at present staff available trained to undertake this major task.

THE STANFORDS

The following case illustrates how a breakdown of one member of the family can reflect the psychopathological problems of the whole family.

Paul Stanford was forty-two years old and a drug addict. In his early thirties he had been a local authority clerical employee, but he had turned increasingly to drugs (sodium amytal), on account of sleeping difficulties. Eventually he managed to obtain large quantities of this drug and, when I met him, was taking forty grains a day (half of this dose would probably be fatal to a normal person). Taken in such quantities the effect of the drug was the opposite of that of a tranquillizer or depressant; as the addict's system got used to it, it acted as a stimulus and provoked vivid sexual fantasies in him, so much so that he actually felt he 'saw' a private striptease show and watched real orgies taking place in his sitting-room. Mr Stanford had lived, apparently satisfied, in this private world for years. Eventually, he poisoned his system so much that he had to be admitted to a mental hospital where, over a period of months, the drug was withdrawn. While in hospital he put on weight and generally recuperated, but he reverted to drugs soon after returning home.

When Mr Stanford was referred to me for the first time in 1954, I visited his home. I found Mrs Stanford to be an attractive woman in her late thirties. There were two children of the marriage. I discovered that the eldest son, aged fifteen, had frequent asthmatic attacks and often had to stay away from school. The second child was eight and also frequently missed school – because of truancy. The only person who did not seem to show any symptoms, or indeed to have any problems, was Mrs Stanford.

Mrs Stanford gave me the impression that she was mildly irritated by her husband sitting at home all day, but she did not show the slightest concern about his taking drugs. In fact it was only after some considerable time that I discovered how much he was taking. She kept the small house neat and tidy, and she looked after her husband and children like any normal housewife. In fact the occasional visitor, as I was then, got the impression of a rather useless man being looked after by his attractive, ill-used wife who was something of a saint.

Over a period of weeks, I became more and more puzzled by the situation, but it was not until I learnt the extent of Mr Stanford's addiction that I first suspected that, beneath the surface of calm affection between husband and wife, there were serious, as yet unarticulated problems. The first clue I had as to what they were was Mr Stanford's admission of his private striptease shows.

When I first visited him he would say very little to me. I noticed that he looked upon me as an unwelcome intruder – that I seemed to be interrupting him in something. He saw me, however, because I arrived on his doorstep in the first instance at the request of the National Assistance Board, who thought he was a drunkard. He continued to resent my visits until one day he started to talk. After assuring himself that I would keep his secret and that his way of life would not be divulged, he told me first that his marriage had broken up many years back. His wife might have been attracted to another man – he didn't know – but soon after the birth of their first child a gradual coolness developed between them and, although they continued to live together, their contact dwindled. For some unknown reason his wife had become disgusted with him and did not want him any more. It was then that he began to suffer from insomnia and subsequently took to drugs.

This case provides a good example of the dangers of too narrow, patient-centred treatment. Mr Stanford's treatment had failed for lack of proper investigation of his home background. Clearly, his drug addiction arose from a marital problem: it was not cause but effect.

Soon after Mr Stanford had told me about his marriage problems and his feelings of rejection, he was able to talk about them to his wife, whom he now blamed for all his misfortunes. Tensions that had lain dormant for years came into the open, and the wounds that husband and wife had inflicted on one another were exposed. It was now evident that both needed help. On my advice, Mr Stanford returned to the hospital and Mrs Stanford was referred to a clinic where a psychiatrist helped her understand her strange and equivocal attitude to her husband. After several months Mr Stanford was clear of addiction and was able to leave hospital. He found a job as a gardener away from London. His wife, after suffering a serious depression while in treatment, regained her contact with him and they began to lead a healthier married life. The eldest boy's asthma remained, but their other son no longer truanted.

THE BROWNS

Another example of family interaction is the story of Peter and his father Colin Brown.

Peter was referred to my department as the 'patient'. He was twenty-three years old, a tall, thin, very withdrawn young man who spent most of his time in his bedroom writing. What he wrote no one knew, as he was most secretive about it, but his father was very concerned about him, as he hardly left the house. If he went out, it was usually late at night and he returned home in the early hours of the morning. He would not say where he went or whom he had met. While he was at grammar school he did very well in most subjects, particularly in English Literature, and his father had hoped that he would enter university. But after he had passed his G.C.E. in a number of 'A' level subjects he 'retired' from life to live on National Assistance. It was about this time that Peter's mother, after years of arguing and fighting with his father, left home and disappeared.

Colin Brown worked in a bank in a London suburb. He was a man of fifty-seven, greying, very conscientious, with high moral principles. He considered that the world was a dangerous place, that humanity on the whole was rotten to the core; he lived only for his religion, in which tolerance strangely had no place. During the time his wife shared his life and Peter was a small boy, most of the arguments were about 'sinful living' (if Mrs Brown put lipstick on) or immorality (if Mrs Brown wanted to see her women-friends). The Browns' home was like a desert island in the sea of suburbia. He would have nothing to do with his neighbours, whom he described as drunkards, because of their occasional parties. He had no friends, either at work or outside. Only on Sunday morning did he move out of his home, to go to church, but even then he sometimes described the sermons as frivolous and decadent. As a small boy Peter was not allowed to play on Sundays, as it was the Lord's day of rest. He usually had to stay in his bedroom reading the Bible, while icy silence descended on the house.

While his mother was still with them, Peter often took her part against his father, but a sudden change came over him after she left. Now everything father said or believed in he confirmed, but he would go even farther than his father: he saw sin everywhere. Not only was the world rotten, but his body too; such a rotten body should rot away, he would say. He did not wash himself, did not shave, just wrote, and wrote . . . and then he would burn his writings.

This state of affairs went on for years, and Colin Brown did not know what to do or where to turn. To admit to others that his son was ill would have implied that his whole way of life was wrong; and *that* he could not face. When he tried to talk to his son, to make him carry on his studies or look for a job, he heard his own words repeated back to him about the sinful, immoral world where Peter had no place. He felt himself caught up in his own self-made web – a tragic, lonely figure living alone without aim or purpose.

One day, he read an article in a local paper about the work my department was doing and, after many sleepless nights, he came forward to seek help.

We were able in time to help Peter to break away from home and start work in publishing, but we could not help his father who, except for his initial approach, kept away and was not willing to see any of my colleagues. Six months after Peter moved away from home Colin Brown committed suicide.

The family does, of course, in many instances contribute positively, of its own accord, towards the recovery of a sick member. If the forces operating in it were all negative, 'family guidance' would be of little use. The therapist's aim must be to fortify these positive aspects, although this may entail unearthing many negative, destructive aspects first. People often ask: 'How can you help these people (the patients) by just talking to them?' The important point to remember is that therapists do not just talk to their patients; in fact, talking takes very much a second place. Much more significant is the patient's own communication to the therapist which can be through words, actions, gestures or silence. It is through this communication that the therapist gains insight and understanding which he can share with his patient.

SUBNORMAL CHILDREN

Not all the problems that arise in the family are the result of dynamic unconscious conflicts between its members. Sometimes fate intervenes from outside. The birth of a subnormal child is an extreme example of this which, besides the tragedy for the child itself, can have a fatal effect on a marriage. If this happens further tragedy arises, as the subnormal child's development will probably be additionally jeopardized.

We do not yet always know why some children are born mentally subnormal or physically handicapped. It is known that subnormal parents tend to reproduce themselves, but highly intelligent people produce subnormal children too. It can happen to happily married as well as to unhappily married couples. So far as we know there are no psychological explanations.

Time and time again when a subnormal child is born the age-old questions are asked: 'Why should it happen to us? What have we done?' Very often this 'we' turns into a second person singular, even if not consciously formulated, and becomes: 'What have *you* done?' And this, to which there is no answer, can easily end in the implied, even if not actually articulated, 'It is your fault, not mine.' If this happens, there is a danger that husband and wife will drift away from each other in body and spirit and come to see their sexuality, which created the child, as a sin and to associate it with primitive, superstitious feelings; for instance, that their bodies are unclean and soaked with invisible bacteria. Love cannot, they think, produce monsters, and so they believe they are cursed. The sickness of the family develops gradually. In the beginning there is silence. The young mother eventually feels that all is not well with her baby. She wants to delay the moment of truth but it comes sooner or later.

Then follow tacit or open accusations and counter-accusations and finally the slow drifting apart.

Even when the disability has been confirmed and faced, there is a grave risk that the parents' relationship with the child will be disturbed. If they become aware of their feeling of guilt, they very often over-protect the child. On the one hand this often hinders his development by cultivating an unnecessary degree of dependency; on the other hand they may make quite exorbitant sacrifices, often at the expense of their own mental health and sometimes that of the other children. If they are unable to face their guilt they may simply reject the child, withdrawing their affections from him, whether or not they reject him physically. Some parents assume their handicapped child is incapable of any development so that they fail to give him the stimulation which he needs to use his limited capacities to the full; others may refuse to accept the diagnosis and drag him from one expert to another in search of some magical cure, while at the same time they may discourage him from doing what he can by never being satisfied with his achievements and always demanding something more.

Thus the parents, as well as the subnormal child, need specialized attention. At present very little indeed is done for the parents of subnormal children. There are now a number of junior and adult training centres for subnormal people, and the teachers who work in these schools often complain that the parents – particularly the mothers – of the patients are difficult and fussy and generally make their work harder. They do not always understand that these mothers are expressing, through their constant complaints, their own feelings for their children. They feel guilty at having produced a subnormal child, and this sense of guilt is often the driving force behind their behaviour. It makes them over-critical and over-sensitive, sometimes to a pathological degree. These mothers are desperately in need of help, attention, and care. It is society's responsibility to help them by relieving them of the burden of their guilt, so that they do not destroy either themselves or their marital relationships. In other words, society must not only pay for junior and adult schools and training centres but, if their work is not to be wasted, it must also provide facilities and staff for a comprehensive family-counselling service.

OLD AGE

The account of the old lady in Chapter 1 suggested how closely loneliness is allied to mental illness. That old age brings family problems needs no labouring. But one example of family worry and individual decline into open mental illness may drive home the need for urgent study of what steps can be taken by society to help in retirement and old age.

It is when people live in retirement without anything to do that they deteriorate most. So often, elderly folk look forward for years to the day when they will no longer have to go out to work, but do not know what to do with themselves when it comes. If they can find purposeful occupation either in being useful to others or in the form of a hobby, the dangers of their age are greatly diminished and the conflicts between them and the younger generation are reduced to a minimum; differences in outlook between people of different ages are mitigated when each has a purpose in life.

MRS SMITH

The case of Mrs Smith illustrates the fate of far too many old people in our society. For years her life centred around bringing up her four children, to whom she devoted all her ability, energy, and love. One by one they left home, until one day she faced the world with nothing to do. For a time she continued, as far as possible, her daily routine with her husband. Then he had a heart-attack and died, and Mrs Smith – now in her seventies – had nothing to do but sit by her window and wait for her children to visit her. As she had lost all sense of purpose, her routine broke down; within months she became obsessed with the idea that she would die of starvation, and started to hide bread and cheese in her wardrobe among her sheets and clothes. On discovering this, the family decided that Mrs Smith could not be left by herself any longer. Apart from hoarding food, she also neglected herself and was generally careless. The neighbours complained that she left the radio on several times during the night, and the milkman often smelt gas coming from the unlit kitchen stove.

A family conference decided that Mrs Smith would have to live with one of her married sons. But soon after the move it was clear that she and her daughter-in-law did not get on. They argued constantly while the son was at work. The old lady had her own views about bringing up her grandchildren and the young Mrs Smith strongly objected to her interference. The old lady then withdrew into her own world because she felt she was useless and unwanted. This situation sparked off an argument between her son and his wife. The son did not want his mother to go into an old peoples' home, but his wife insisted that she could not live with her. Eventually he had to make the tragic choice; either his wife or his mother must leave. The choice fell on the mother.

Mrs Smith senior was admitted to an old people's home where her condition deteriorated. Away from her familiar way of life and with no interests to occupy her time, her imagination soon got the better of her. She began to hear voices and suffer from hallucinations about the past. Gradually, she became more and more depressed and finally had to be admitted to a mental hospital, where she died.

There are many stories like that of Mrs Smith; a tremendous amount remains to be done in providing facilities, such as homes, day centres, and special hospitals, to enable the elderly to live independently of their families if necessary. Once this becomes the norm, contact between old people and their young families will be subject to far less strain and the old people themselves may become less prone to the depression that all too easily leads to the apathetic, hopeless world of the geriatric patient ward of a mental hospital.

MARITAL COUNSELLING

There is no such thing, outside the realms of imagination, as a marriage that is free from conflict. Such a relationship is not in the nature of human beings . . .*

Many cases of mental illness in adults or maladjustment in children prove to be the outcome of severe marital problems. Marital counselling is one of the most recent developments in community care, and one of its pioneer organizations is the Family Discussion Bureau (F.D.B.). Started in 1948 by the Family Welfare Association, the F.D.B. attached itself in 1956 to the Tavistock Institute of Human Relations. Since its foundation it has made a very great contribution both to the understanding of family relationships and to the study of the technique of marriage counselling itself.

It was recognized from the start that in marital difficulties one is confronted with the same type of disturbance in

* *Marriage: Studies in Emotional Conflict and Growth.* Family Discussion Bureau, Methuen, 1960.

human relationships that psychoanalysts studied in various settings, and on which psychoanalysts have thrown so much light. It was to psychoanalysis therefore that the case-workers of the Bureau turned for assistance in the twofold task of trying to deepen their understanding of the nature of marital relationships and of developing a casework technique of a rational aetiological basis, which could be learned and used by caseworkers who were not themselves psycho-analytically trained.*

Some of the F.D.B.'s teaching was done in conjunction with psychiatric social work in Middlesex, where it was possible to put into practice the theory first discussed in seminars and courses.

Before the F.D.B. existed, the greatest emphasis in this kind of social work was put on the personal relationship between case-worker and patient. Underlying almost all practical case work was the theory of transference which had been taken over from psychoanalysis. The F.D.B. were the first to teach that, while the relationship between a case-worker and patient is naturally of importance, it is much more important to know and interpret the relationship between the marital partners themselves.

The following case, from my own experience, gives an illustration of how such an approach works in practice.

An Inspector of the National Society for the Prevention of Cruelty to Children (N.S.P.C.C.) reported a case to the community care service of a five-year-old girl who was apparently neglected by her mother. On closer inquiry, he found that the neglect was not as serious as first reported by the neighbours, and was connected with the parents' own serious emotional problems, for which they needed help.

* ibid.

The family consisted of a husband in his late thirties, his wife in her late twenties, the five-year-old daughter, and a little boy of two. The neighbours had complained that they often heard the husband and wife quarrelling, sometimes late at night or early in the morning, and at these times they also heard the little girl screaming.

When I went in to see this couple I found that they were only too eager to share their problems with me. I discovered that, as a soldier, the husband had been ill-treated in a Japanese P.O.W. camp and that since his return he had suffered from nightmares about a Japanese soldier who attacked and tortured him. He also 'saw' this Japanese soldier, whenever he got angry, often standing in the middle of the room staring at him. He had hoped that with the passing of years this would happen less and less, but in fact it happened more and more. When his wife was angry with him or they quarrelled together he often no longer saw her but the Japanese soldier about to torture him. He would then attack his wife and beat her. Not until he had come to his senses did he realize what he had done, when he felt deep guilt and remorse.

I also discovered that the wife was illegitimate and was obsessed with the idea of finding out who her parents were. Her illegitimacy had given her a guilty feeling that she was being punished for something. She felt unable to love her daughter as much as she wanted to because she was envious of her having parents, although she tried to convince herself that such feelings were unreasonable and harmful. As it was the sex act that had caused her illegitimacy she also strongly resisted all her husband's sexual advances, which he often made when he was frightened or lonely and most wanted her.

Consequently, the husband felt that the wife was torturing him and identified her with the Japanese soldier, while the wife saw in the husband the embodiment of sex – the root of all that was most evil to her in the world. Nevertheless, despite this extreme mutual rejection, there still remained a residue of love between them. A woman colleague visited the husband and I the wife, and it eventually became possible for them not only to tell us their fears and frustrations but also to tell each other. After a long time, they gradually came to realize that what they were fighting were non-existent ghosts of the past which had nothing to do with reality, and they were then able to re-establish contact and begin to lead a normal life.

Chapter 3

HOSPITAL CARE:
Atmosphere, Admission, and Treatment

ATMOSPHERE

SOME mentally ill patients manage with home care or with periodic attendance at day hospitals or out-patient clinics. These are discussed in Chapter 4. Others, however, have to go into hospital, perhaps because their relatives cannot cope with them while they are ill, because they have no one to look after them, or because they need special treatment; they may only have to enter hospital for a short period or during moments of crisis, but the atmosphere of mental hospitals must be part of this book. Experience inside hospital may affect drastically the social worker's task in community care. The way in which a patient is admitted, his ability to keep in contact with his relatives, the length of his stay, his preparation for discharge, all affect his chances of recuperation and his ability to make an effective return to the community. His attitude and behaviour when he returns home will be greatly influenced by the treatment he has received in hospital, not only from the doctor but also from the nurses and other staff.

ADMISSION

To enter a mental hospital and stay in it as a patient is always a dramatic experience. In physical diseases the doctors deal with something which is 'there', and while, of course, in a great many mental illnesses with a physical basis there is also a cause which can be located, on the whole the location of emotional disturbance is indefinable; this makes it mysterious and uncanny, while the treatment smacks of magic – or hocus-pocus. In physical diseases there is a good chance that the cause, once found, can be effectively treated. An intelligent person who is mentally ill knows that, because the causes of mental illness are so complicated, something as straightforward is seldom possible.

Both physical and mental illness which must be treated in hospital for any length of time often involves a loss of status and sometimes bring about financial hardship for the family. In physical illness the period of hospitalization is often predictable. The patient in a mental hospital, on the other hand, does not know how long he may have to stay there. It may be weeks, months, or perhaps even years. Moreover when he does leave hospital he has to come to terms not only with the after-effects of his illness but also with the stigma which is still associated with having been in a mental hospital. Short-term physical illness may handicap the patient temporarily from following his old pursuits, interests, sports, and other forms of physical activities in the home, but generally speaking he will be able to resume his ordinary life both in society and in the home. Again, this may not be the case with the mentally ill who may have been away from home for a much longer time. Society and the patient's environment may view the physically ill with great sympathy. He may be visited in hospital by a great many friends and relatives, who will bring him presents and wish him a speedy recovery. Mental hospitals, on the other hand, are still a source of anxiety to the community. Fewer people visit a patient in a mental hospital, and he often feels that they visit him reluctantly. Moreover, he can never be at ease with friends who come to see him, not only because of his own mental state, but because of the disturbed environment, which he feels affects his visitors.

Finally, the stigma of mental hospitals still exists. The fear of mental illness, the fear of loss of sanity and control is very strong in every member of society. Mental hospitals still remind ordinary 'normal' men and women that there are forces within them which act independently and can upset the equilibrium of the mind. Because of this fear, and because of the reality of the mental hospital situation, the patient may also not see his children for many months.

There is at present a tendency to say that mental illness is just like physical illness and that mental hospitals are just like other hospitals. This, of course, is not true and nothing is gained by minimizing the differences between the two situations. It is true that mental hospitals nowadays are not the same as they used to be. There is less violence than in the past, partly because of modern drug treatment, which can control extreme behaviour, and partly because of changed ideas and more cheerful environments. However, these hospitals are still often huge institutions, sometimes with two to three thousand beds; they are old buildings housing old asylums, and it will be a long time yet before small units attached to general hospitals become at all common.

To return to the moment of admission, whether as an 'informal' patient or under one of the procedures for compulsory admittance – to enter hospital for the first time as a patient creates anxieties which are partly based on the nature of the illness itself, partly on reality, and very often on both. I remember when I worked as a trainee in a mental hospital a patient described vividly his first impressions as he was driven by car through the large gates:

The car slowed down and the driver hooted his horn. A uniformed man came out from the porter's lodge. He looked like a policeman or a warder in a prison. He had a bunch of keys, perhaps twenty of them, which made a clanking noise as he walked towards the gates. He opened the gates and signalled for the car to stop. He looked at me and asked the driver, 'What's his name?' He didn't ask me, and this itself made me feel like a child who couldn't even speak. He directed the driver to the admission ward. The car started, and the first sign I saw was 'Dead Slow'. I now know this is stupid, but the word 'Dead' meant something more to me than just a traffic indication. . . . I soon noticed other people – my fellow patients – walking slowly, some of them dragging themselves about, in the beautiful gardens. Some were mumbling to themselves, others were standing like stone statues. I said to myself: 'Tomorrow, I shall be one of them.' I wanted to turn back, I felt like running, but I knew that the gates were locked, that the uniformed man had taken his keys with him, and that there was no way out.

This patient's experience is not unique. Even though the gates may not be locked and although in some hospitals most of them have disappeared, the mental patient faces a cold reception. In his sensitiveness and fear he picks up little signs which he may misinterpret. His very first meeting in the hospital is with the porter and, within the hospital, the administrators. None of these people will have had any training in human relationships or even on how to approach the patient. First impressions will last for ever and can sometimes be very damaging, however good the medical treatment or nursing may be.

We have come a long way since the world of Bedlam when, on Sunday afternoons, the public would watch the 'lunatics' as objects of amusement. However, we still think in terms of specialists – doctors doing their bit, nurses, gatekeepers, and administrators theirs, and so on – and there is still a danger that, approached simply as a job of work, the treatment of human misery and unhappiness remains inhumane. If the National Health Service is to achieve high standards, changes have to occur at many levels. Not only do we have to build better hospitals with fewer beds, not only do we have to have an excellent medical and nursing service, but we must, by careful selection and training, see that these services are imbued with the best values of humanity. At all times we must be aware that our responsibility lies not only with the patient but also with his relatives. We must prevent at all costs unnecessary pain, tension, and anxiety in those who leave the patient at the hospital gates and return to their ordinary lives.

In 1963 the mother of a sixteen-year-old boy came to see me, and complained bitterly about the way she had been treated when she took her son Gordon to a mental hospital. Gordon had been in an extremely disturbed condition for the past few months and eventually the parents, acting on psychiatric advice, decided that he should be admitted to hospital. On arrival, Gordon's mother tried to get hold of a doctor to find out what was going to happen to her son and what sort of treatment he would receive. After a long wait a young woman doctor appeared whom she described as 'extremely cold and professional like'. She did not show any concern, was 'haughty', and told the mother that 'these cases do not recover'. The mother told me that on hearing this, standing in a cold draughty corridor, she truly felt as if she had stepped out of a dimension of reality. It was her son; she had carried him in her body for nine months; she had borne him; she had watched him grow from a micro-organism into a human being; she was there when he cried because of hunger, pain, or loneliness. This child was a part of her life, and now that she had to part with him, perhaps for ever, she had to face an immense crisis in which she badly needed the support and concern of everyone around her.

Gordon was assigned a ward with people who were old enough to be his grandparents, and when his

mother protested the doctor told her that there was no
adolescent ward in the hospital. She felt that it was
wrong that a young man should spend his life among
old people, but there was no alternative. What really
pained her was that the doctor said that the only treatment that could help Gordon would be psychoanalysis,
but that would cost at least ten pounds a week. 'As you
can't afford it,' she was told, 'there is nothing else to do.'

This mother left the hospital in a state of anxiety and
fear greater than she had ever experienced, although
she had had a lot of trouble with her son since the onset
of his illness. When she told this story to her husband he
cried all night and could not go to work for several days
afterwards.

Administrators, nurses, and doctors do not always
realize that they have a primary function not only towards the patient but also towards the relatives, and it
is very little use for the mental welfare officer to prepare
patients and relatives if the moments of reception are
gravely traumatic.

I accompanied a patient and his wife to a hospital
some time ago. The man, aged fifty-two, had incurred a
brain injury in a car accident and had become insane.
On arrival at the hospital we had to wait alone in an
empty corridor and for forty minutes no one talked to
us. Neither nurses nor doctors had much time for the
wife later and she developed a tremendous feeling of
guilt for having left her husband 'in such a place'.

HOSPITAL PRACTICE

Fortunately, such stories as these are not the whole
truth. Miss Ann Broadhurst, a psychologist, described
to me the Professorial Unit at the Queen Elizabeth
Hospital, Birmingham, which consists of a ward con-
taining psychiatric patients in a general hospital. In-

patients are accommodated in small rooms like bed-sitting rooms, some double, some single, and some for three or four patients. The ward also includes a laundry, dining-room and kitchen, and a clinical room where all physical procedures are carried out. Patients bring many of their personal belongings and clothing at the beginning of their stay, which is not allowed in other hospitals, and while on the ward they are encouraged to lead as active and normal a life as possible. They take some part in routine ward-cleaning and share in cooking for themselves and for other patients as well as doing their personal laundry.

The routine of the ward is quite unlike that of medical and surgical wards. Routine recording, such as temperature charts, is discarded in favour of more meaningful daily notes of patients' behaviour, moods, activities, and treatments. Naturally, where physical illness is also found it is investigated and treated as with any patient in hospital. But the emphasis is more on domestic life in a large, if somewhat unusual, 'family' community.

Into this community are admitted psychiatric patients of all types for observation and treatment. The layout of the ward provides accommodation for both men and women patients – a most unusual feature in a general hospital, but it has been found to work smoothly and contributes to the normal community atmosphere of the unit. Special sleeping accommodation in small units also enables the admission of mothers with young babies; on one occasion a man and his wife, who were both considered to be in need of psychiatric treatment, were allowed in together.

Surprising as it may seem, severely disturbed and even suicidal patients have not only been successfully managed in this setting, but they have not caused undue anxiety among those less ill. Any disturbances which arise are discussed and used therapeutically.

Patients are expected to adhere to a time-table which gives some sense of structure to the day and provides for a variety of activities. As a matter of policy, television is excluded from the ward, as it is believed to discourage initiative and more active forms of recreation. Organized daytime activities include dancing, physical training, occupational therapy and art therapy, discussion groups, relaxation classes, and visits to entertainments in the neighbourhood, such as ice-skating, films, plays, and classes in beauty treatment. There are also evening socials. Patients may go for walks and shopping expeditions, and visitors are usually permitted daily (unlike in many other hospitals where visiting is allowed only once or twice a week). Patients who are students are encouraged to continue their studies.

Patients in this unit receive physical treatment or psychotherapy as considered appropriate, but the emphasis in treatment is on an understanding of the others in the small community, which is quite deliberately made as similar to a normal community as possible. Patients meet regularly for discussion of routine and personal problems and some interpretation of these problems may be made. Patient management is also discussed informally at meetings of the entire staff of the unit, which consists of psychiatrists, psychologists, psychiatric social workers, and occupational therapists, as well as nurses and nursing students.

Visitors to the unit are invariably struck by the formal and homely atmosphere, both for patients and for staff members. This is deliberately cultivated as an important part of the treatment. On discharge, patients are encouraged and helped to return to or to find new jobs, and may even sleep in the hospital and go out to work daily. Alternatively ex-patients may return for day treatment, although the unit does not primarily cater for this class of patient.

Mr Peter Hunter, the Senior Psychiatric Social Worker in a hospital in South Devon, reports:

In 1952 this Hospital admitted 470 patients and discharged 400. In 1962 it admitted 1,033 patients and discharged 860. These simple facts illustrate the changing position of the Mental Health services, during which time the framework of law and administration in which we function has been radically altered by the 1959 Mental Health Act. With the increasing rate of admission and discharge we have found that Social Workers have been brought more and more into the direct treatment situation with patients (rather than families and other agencies) who now form the major part of our caseload. With our present medical and social worker staffing position, it may be that this is inevitable and we must accept the position; nevertheless we should think about the consequences. Traditionally, the role of the Social Worker in a Mental Hospital was seen as being principally concerned with the families of the mentally ill, and it is this aspect of the work that is now being neglected because of other pressures. I have already mentioned the general increase in the number of patients as one cause of this changing role – another lies in the present national arrangements for 'Community Care'. With easier admission and discharge from mental hospital, with a national figure of 47·5 per cent re-admissions, and the evidence of our own experience to call upon, we know there are now mentally sick people living in the community who need constant care and treatment. Psychiatrists, apart from their domiciliary consultations which most usually are associated with a patient's admission to hospital, are almost totally tied to clinics and hospitals and offer no treatment directly to the patient at home. The implication of this is that the Social Worker and General Practitioner are left to work with the most disturbed patients in the community, who, because of their condition, are not usually able to cooperate in a clinic based treatment programme. It will be said that the number of patients concerned is small, but the amount of distur-bance caused, particularly in families, is large. It is painful to consider that without effective community services (and these should be flexible enough to allow the psychiatrist to treat patients at home if necessary) this policy may lead to an increase in the amount of psychiatric disorder in the next generation. Our growing concern with this problem is I hope being reflected in our work, but effective action lies not in recognition of the problem, but in increasing the number of one's professional staff.

The report continues:

Between October 1962 and March 1963, Miss S. Regnart, Psychiatric Social Worker, made a follow-up study of patients who discharged themselves against medical advice in the period January to June 1961. The group consisted of 56 patients, and was 12·7 per cent of the total number of discharges during the six months concerned. The most significant factor was the high rate of re-admission in the first three months after discharge. . . . 60·6 per cent of the patients who left hospital in this way returned in this period of time, as against 32·5 per cent for all patients (including the group under study). Again, this high re-admission rate must mean a great deal of disturbance and unhappiness for individual families, and calls for intensive help, particularly within the first three months out of hospital.*

THE LONG-STAY PATIENT

Former practice can sometimes serve as a guide in establishing our own attitudes, and although the gap between us and the past is perhaps too great for this to apply in respect of mental illness, it is worth remembering that in many communities in the Middle Ages, for religious reasons, the mentally ill were accepted into the

* *Annual Report of the Psychiatric Social Work Department*, Moorhaven Hospital, Ivybridge, South Devon, October 1962–September 1963.

midst of normal social life. This practice is hardly likely
to survive in our large industrial cities – though it may
still be possible in smaller communities. The special
problem of the 'long-stay' patient therefore still remains
important.

Professor Kathleen Jones of the University of York
has written:

Though a good deal of work has been done on the movement
of short-stay patients, there is very little evidence on the
character of present long-stay mental hospital populations,
or on the rate at which they are being replaced. Examination
of the long-stay patients in one large mental hospital established that nearly half of them could be expected to be
alive in fifteen years' time, and that most of them were
quite unfitted by personal capacity or family situation for a
return to the community.

No doubt these patients *could* be discharged. The act of
discharging a patient is in itself relatively simple. The statement that a patient has been discharged tells us only that he
has left the hospital, not what the hospital has done for him,
in what state he is now, or what the community can do for
him. A 'liberal' discharge policy is a kindness to some
patients; it could be an instrument of cruelty to others. We
should be unwise to place too much reliance on discharge
statistics, or to regard them as an index of success.*

The Ministry of Health proposes to halve the number
of psychiatric beds in hospitals by 1975, but unless there
are adequate preventive and after-care facilities in the
community this plan may have disastrous effects. There
are still a great many people who are not ready to leave
hospital. Some of these need prolonged specialist care,
some are homeless or unfitted to live at home, others
have disturbed relationships with their families which
are likely to cause early relapse and which cannot be

* Kathleen Jones, in *Medical Care*, Vol. 1, No. 3, p. 160, July–
September 1962.

improved.* There is a danger of extremes, of closing too many hospital wards on the one hand before there are enough fully manned community care services to care for all the patients living at home, or of creating institutionalization, on the other hand. Whereas in the past many patients did tend to stay too long in hospitals, clear distinction must be made between those for whom home care is suitable and those who need to be in hospital for treatment.

THE DANGER OF INSTITUTIONALIZATION

Many people who spend a very long time in a closed community tend to find a greater sense of belonging, of being involved in that community, than in the outside world. This is particularly the case with long-stay mental patients in the big, older hospitals. But the problem is not only one of breaking the patient's excessive dependence on the hospital and its staff before discharge, and of overcoming their fears of life outside, but rather of never allowing this excessive dependence to build up in the first place. The prevention of this is one of the major aims of the therapeutic community.† The positive angle on institutionalization is to see that the patient's links with his family and friends, with his workmates and neighbours, are not entirely broken when he enters hospital; alienation from family and community is at the roots of institutionalization. At present the stigma attached to mental illness and mental hospitals, the awkward visiting hours, the gloomy surroundings in which to meet, the inaccessible

* George W. Brown, 'Changing Patterns of Care of the Schizophrenic Patient', in *The British Journal of Psychiatric Social Work*, Vol. VII, 1963, No. 1.

† John Cumming and Elane Cumming, in *Ego and Milieu*, Tavistock Publications, 1964.

situation of some hospitals, do little to encourage visitors. All too often the way in which relatives were treated when the patient was admitted does nothing to allay their fears.

A much more positive attitude towards relatives is needed. An explanation at the outset of the nature of the patient's illness, some indication of the probable duration of his stay, encouragement to visit him, and preparation for short visits home help to encourage visitors and keep contacts alive.

If the family does not visit and the patient becomes cut off from the outside world, he often becomes apathetic and slides deeper and deeper into hospital routine until it becomes his whole life. In a big hospital a patient can become such a tiny cog that he drifts through the years scarcely noticed.

Unfortunately, the level of care and attention varies to a very great extent from hospital to hospital. It is very unlikely that, in a good hospital, with a community atmosphere, any patient could be forgotten. Nevertheless, there still remains a very great danger that in overcrowded and understaffed hospitals a patient might become merely a name on a list, with nobody concerned for his future.

In a hospital which has three thousand beds and only a few overworked doctors, they cannot be expected to do more than see the patient once in a while and leave the rest to the nurses. To speak of psychotherapy under such conditions is a delusion. So most patients, after receiving their initial treatment, which might consist of E.C.T. (electric convulsive therapy), insulin, or some other form of drug treatment, may never see a doctor for weeks on end. If these methods are effective the patient is lucky, if not he can in time be forgotten and, unless there is a highly skilled nursing staff, may spend many years in the hospital.

Through the introduction of modern methods and the community approach, where patients are seen at ward meetings in groups, these dangers are to some extent reduced. However, there are still thousands of patients in mental hospitals whose original symptoms have disappeared but who have become so institutionalized that they no longer have any desire to leave. They have nowhere to go and would need a great deal of training and care to help them to adjust to life outside. It is strange to see how difficult it is for some patients to fit into a hospital and yet how, after they have settled down to the routine and the security it provides, the pull of hospital life is so strong that they have great difficulties in leaving, even if their symptoms have cleared up. The problem of institutionalization is then superimposed on the illness which may have disappeared or have altered for the better.

Chapter 4

HOSPITAL CARE

DISCHARGE AND REHABILITATION

UNLESS a patient undergoes thorough preparation before discharge into the world outside, he will have little chance of coming to terms with it. Such preparation not only entails discussion of his anxieties and problems but also information as to what facilities are open to him when he leaves and how he can use them, what National Assistance is and how much he is entitled to, what sort of forms he will be confronted with and how to fill them up. In general, he needs to know of the usual demands society makes on its citizens.

Moreover, if similar preparation is not given to the relatives – or to those responsible for him – who may well be alienated from him at this stage anyway unless they have been encouraged to keep in contact, his return could well end in another terrible fiasco. Nowadays, it is usually the policy to discharge patients as soon as possible, often without due regard to the grave consequences of premature discharges.

The preparation of the patient to return to his place in the life of the community should in fact start the very moment he enters the hospital. The hospital might come to be and to be seen to be part of the community services. Some hospitals have their own sheltered workshops (apart from the occupational therapy department) where patients can prepare themselves for competitive employment in the community. Others allow the patient to go to work by day and come back at night. But life outside the hospital walls may not be easy

for a patient who has become used to the safety and
security of routine inside.

Leaving a mental hospital, particularly after a long
time, is a great challenge. Even if his symptoms have
disappeared or subsided, the question that faces the
patient is whether he will be acceptable to the world
outside and whether he will be able to accept that
world. Many patients tell me that a new crisis, which
may or may not be connected with the problems which
led to the original breakdown, develops at this stage.

A patient who had been in hospital for a few years
described an afternoon a few weeks before his discharge. He had already had some afternoons in the
village and also in the nearby town, but he always
knew that he 'belonged' somewhere. On this particular
Saturday afternoon he found himself standing in the
High Street of the small town watching the comings and
goings with a completely different awareness. He knew
now that before long he would be expected to become a
part of the busy crowd shopping and rushing about its
business, and this filled him with great loneliness and
anxiety. What would happen to him? Where, in a
world he found cold and unfriendly, would he be
accepted? Whom could he talk with about his problems? What if he could not bear his loneliness? This
patient, a man of forty-five, had no one in the world
outside the hospital. His parents had died, other relatives had disappeared over the years, and he had no
friends – he had once had a woman friend, but he felt
she must have married by now. As he stood looking on
he became increasingly sure that it was not possible for
him to leave the hospital. The voices that used to speak
to him so loudly in the past were silent; he had had no
hallucinations for a long time, yet he felt that he was
not 'normal'.

As evening fell, he watched the day changing and

growing dark. His apprehension grew. There were more young people about now, going dancing or queueing up in front of the cinema. As he walked on, he looked at the houses in the side streets. In some the curtains were drawn, but in others he could see through the windows to the families sitting together. Would he ever become a part of a family? Would he ever belong anywhere? He felt as if those houses were watching him – as if the windows were eyes staring at his loneliness. This man did not feel he belonged in the outside world because his contact with it had lapsed while he was in hospital; nothing remained to connect his inner world with that outside. The result was that he drew back from the normal world and actually developed a fear of going beyond the hospital gates.

While there are some patients like this one who cannot leave, or long to return after leaving, there are others who do manage the transition back to society. This is largely dependent on whether the hospital itself has successfully established contact with the world outside.

In Warlingham Park Hospital, Surrey, the clinical facilities have for a long time been extended into the community, and local clinical and social teams in the mental health services have been coordinated to help the rehabilitation work of the hospital.

The hospital has established a rehabilitation unit within its walls which is equipped to prepare the patient for his return to the community. There are three stages in this process: the attempt to restore the patient to his maximum clinical and social level, the preparation of the community to receive him and, finally, the provision of support for the patient and his relatives and friends when he leaves. Whenever possible he is discharged to his home, but if for any reason this is not possible or desirable an effort is made to place him in the mental after-care hostel in Croydon or in private lodgings. In certain cases a 'boarding-out officer' helps to arrange suitable accommodation with landladies, and the rent may be subsidized by the local authority.

As I have just mentioned, it is not always desirable to discharge a patient to his own home. George W. Brown's researches with schizophrenics showed that:

Success in staying out of hospital was related to the type of living group to which the patient returned. Patients who returned to parents or wives did worse and were more likely to be readmitted in the year after discharge than those returning to more distantly related kin or to lodgings. There are a number of different explanations of this finding, of which one is obviously that more severely ill patients were accepted by close relatives. However, analysis indicated that home life may well have directly brought about some of the deterioration in behaviour. For example:

(i) Outbursts of violence or temper occurred relatively less frequently in those living with siblings or in lodgings, although the prevalence of frank psychotic symptoms was similar.

(ii) Those patients who were in contact with their mothers throughout the day were more likely to be readmitted than those who went out to work or whose mothers did so.

(iii) There were fewer readmissions amongst those returning to a household other than that from which they were admitted. Such a result may be interpreted as due in part to the avoidance of previously stressful environments.

It was tentatively concluded that it might not always be best for a schizophrenic patient to return to the close emotional ties often found with parents and wives.*

The alternatives to home discharge are discussed in the next chapter.

* George W. Brown, 'Changing Patterns of Care of the Schizophrenic Patient', in *British Journal of Psychiatric Social Work*, Vol. VII, 1963.

The patient who spends only a few months 'inside' may retain the pattern, the routine, of the outer world in his memory, and, provided he is able to keep in touch with his relatives and friends, the decision to leave may not cause very great pain. Some serious problems are, however, bound to arise.

The short-stay patient will remember the period leading up to his admission to the hospital, his unreasonable behaviour, or the eccentric things he said and did at home and at work, and he will worry about whether he can live all this down. If he has had a chance to discuss his fears, anxieties, and uncertainties with the hospital staff – with doctors and social workers – and knows that they have kept in touch with his family during these difficult months, he will probably leave with more confidence. However, with the high discharge rate of a large mental hospital and the relatively few doctors and social workers available, many patients and their families will not have received such help. In most mental hospitals at present preparation for the patient's return to the community is still very haphazard; because of the administrative divisions between the responsibility of the hospital and the local authority there is no clear-cut policy as to who should undertake it. Should the local authority social worker keep in touch with the patient throughout his stay in hospital? Or should the psychiatric social worker in the hospital deal with him while he is there? Who should follow up the patient after his discharge? Who decides, and on what basis, whether hospital social workers should visit patients, or whether it should be personnel from local authorities? Too often, nobody does anything.

While lip-service is constantly paid to the importance of community care, and 'cooperation' between the hospital and local authority services, the quality of such cooperation is very varied: at a maximum level it is very good and at a minimum level it is non-existent. One mental health department covers an area of a large mental hospital in London which admitted 1,000 patients in 1964, discharged just under 1,000, and re-admitted nearly 500; yet it has received only eighteen cases for after-care from the hospital since the beginning of 1962, and most of the discharged patients do not receive any help direct from the hospital.

The reasons for this non-cooperation are many. To begin with, some large hospitals with the death sentence hanging over them (most of them are scheduled to disappear by 1975) view local authority community care with suspicion and consider it a potential threat to their existence. In addition, the tradition of mental hospitals differs a great deal from those of community care. In the former the doctor is the key figure and directs the social work activities, while in the latter these are more the responsibility of the social workers themselves. Such freedom of action is viewed by the medical profession with great suspicion, and while doctors are willing to concede that local authority community care services may be essential, they would like them to be under control of the hospital. Yet, as the P.E.P.* pointed out, psychiatric social work has a greater chance of developing within the local authority structure. In fact, they recommended moving psychiatric social workers from the hospitals into the community.

One criticism of the present system is that, in some mental hospitals, psychiatric social workers cannot use their professional skills to the full and have to do routine paper work which could be done by less qualified personnel.

The idea that social workers should always belong

* Political and Economic Planning, *Problems and Progress in Medical Care*, Nuffield Provincial Hospital Trust, O.U.P.

to the medical team is one of the traditions of psychiatric social work training which often does not give psychiatric social workers the right encouragement to take independent action within the team. Both in community care and in the hospital it is naturally of the utmost importance that medical advice should be available to the social worker, but, except where necessary for clinical reasons, this advice should not mean direction of the social worker's activities.

To sum up: this at present ill-defined division between the hospital and the local authorities aggravates in particular the problems of the long-stay patient. There is a danger that he will become so institutionalized that, superimposed on his original illness, there will be a further problem – his inability to cope with life outside the hospital. Hospital routine has demanded conformity, and the conforming patient finds it impossible to restart his life, as he is often asked to do after many years, without the safety and security of this routine. The very conformity that was demanded of him has robbed him of initiative and self-reliance and now stands in his way.

Dr Freeman pointed out what a dramatic effect home treatment, day hospital treatment, and out-patient clinics had on admission and readmission to hospitals and the chances of successful discharge.* He reported that in 1958 admissions to Graylingwell Hospital were down by 61·7 per cent in the Worthing area, and 50 per cent in the Chichester area, on the figures for 1956.

In Worthing the mental health service carries out extensive domiciliary visiting, very similar to the scheme under Professor Querido, who organized the Amsterdam Mental Health Services. Whenever a mental

* Dr H. L. Freeman, 'Psychiatric Day Hospitals', in *Oxford Medical School Gazette*, Vol. 2, p. 119, 1959.

breakdown occurs, doctors and health visitors go immediately to the patient, and much of the treatment is carried out in his home. However, such schemes as those in Worthing and Amsterdam can be really effective only if close links are built between day hospitals and mental hospitals. (These links do in fact exist between Worthing and Chichester day hospitals and Graylingwell Hospital.)

It seems that the discharge of patients from hospitals (of whatever category) falls into two periods:

During the first three or four weeks following discharge, most patients sought some kind of reassurance that the hospital was still available to them. . . .

Later, however:

Instead of looking forward to seeing the doctor and welcoming the benefit inside of the hospital, they avoided it altogether and wanted to know for how long they needed to continue on medication. One man who lived in lodgings near the hospital would make a detour of half a mile to avoid passing it. He had been in hospital twenty years and had been quite reluctant to leave. In many, many cases, it probably took more than a year for them to lose their fear of the hospital. Until they had gained some roots, and felt they belonged to a new community, there remained in them a failure, leading to a return to hospital.*

A patient who was discharged from hospital after several years described his first day in lodgings in a way that makes very understandable the need for reassurance in the first period.

I took some sedatives the previous night and I slept through like a log. But when I opened my eyes it took me what seemed a very long time until I was able to gather my

* W. B. Harbert, 'Social Work with Long Stay Psychiatric Patients', in *Case Conference*, Vol. 8, No. 4, September 1961.

thoughts together. Even then, when I realized that I was alone in my room, and there were no other patients in the ward with me, I was listening for the routine noises of the morning which were so familiar to me by now. The rattle of the trolleys to and fro from the kitchen; the blurred voices of the kitchen staff. Lying in bed I was waiting for the nurse to call to get dressed. The anti-climax in the realization that these familiar happenings were absent gave me a strange feeling of insecurity.

At home, with neighbours, and at work anxieties and practical problems crowd in on the discharged patient.

One patient remembers the first day at home with his wife, with whom he had not shared the same bed for many years. He awoke to find her watching him with an expression which he thought was full of anxiety and puzzlement. When he asked her what was the matter she was reluctant to say at first, but later admitted that she could not sleep all night because she was frightened at what he might do to her. This patient said that this confession, in an entirely unfamiliar world, by a strange woman who was none the less his wife and whom he was trying to woo back, made him completely impotent.

A patient, who had come out of hospital after seventeen years, recalls an interview with a prospective employer. He decided to be frank and tell him that he had been in a mental hospital for some time. He also told him that he had previously heard voices, but explained that he was now well and wanted to work. The employer interrupted him in the middle of his explanation, left the room, and sent in the personnel manager with a prepared excuse for not offering him a job after all. Ever since then, said this former patient, he had kept quiet about his mental illness. As a result he suffered continually from a deep anxiety that he would be 'found out'. He said that he felt like a criminal, and added: 'Even criminals are in a better position nowadays. To be mentally ill is worse than being a murderer.'

There is yet a further problem that a patient returning to the community has to face. Even if his employer knows his full background, it is difficult for him to know how much he can say to his workmates. If his lack of skill and lack of confidence show they are bound to notice it, and patients often find that fellow workers may be less sympathetic than employers and, if the occasion arises, even use the fact that someone has been mentally ill to harry him at the slightest provocation. Tea and lunch breaks can be anxious times for a patient.

A married woman with two children, who had only been in hospital for eighteen months, once told me in tears of the reception given her by the neighbours. Her children asked her why their friends no longer came to visit them. It was quite clear to her that their mothers had prevented them from coming because of where she had been.

In this world, where there are wealthy organizations for the prevention of cruelty to animals, 50 per cent of those suffering from any form of mental illness may well face such a reception when they return home and try to settle down again. Even if they are now quite well again this can be a shattering experience. Even for the strong it is sometimes difficult to stand up to the enmity and suspicion of a hostile community. How much more difficult is it for the weak! The mentally ill in the community need a great deal of help – both the patients and their relations. Without this help their original subjective problems may be replaced by serious objective social problems of ostracism and prejudice.

PREMATURE DISCHARGE

Relatives face a serious, even dangerous, situation if a patient is discharged without the necessary preparation, particularly essential if he has suffered from delusions or hallucinations. The Mental Health Act of 1959 emphasizes the treatment of the mentally ill in their habitual environment, but it is gravely irresponsible to discharge patients if they are not ready, particularly if the after-care facilities of the local authority are not equipped to give them the help they need. Nor is it only the patients themselves who need preparation. Families, too, must be ready to receive them with the right kind of help and sympathy; all too often families who look forward to welcoming their relatives back from hospital find themselves quite at a loss when they do eventually return. A man, for instance, who has a persecution complex may easily have a damaging effect on his wife and his children (most children identify with their parents and if the parent is psychotic this can have serious consequences). Relatives complain frequently that hospitals have discharged psychotics whom they cannot control and who infect the young with their illness.

Adequate community services, day hospitals, and day centres can help in some, but not all, cases of premature discharge. There are, however, some situations which should never be allowed to arise. How can a man, for example, live with a psychotic wife whose delusion is that he is unfaithful to her? How can anyone expect children to flourish in such a situation? The following letter speaks for itself:

My husband's breakdown occurred three years ago, was quickly recognized by our G.P. and referred to hospital. He refused to enter voluntarily and eventually was taken in and later certified. He was, however, allowed to go to work although he 'promised' the doctor not to visit me. He did at all odd hours of the day, and so I agreed to have him home again. Later he returned to the hospital for treatment and when he came out I hoped that despite the fact that his breakdown took the form of a delusion that I had been unfaithful, our life might continue as before.

My husband is abusive towards me; tells lies about me to my family, friends and eldest daughter; he sometimes hits me; one must tell him to do things like one tells a child; his reactions are unpredictable; his behaviour is irrational; he is still suspicious of me and everyone connected with me. He has no insight, and it is this above all that is hardest to bear, for I live with a man who cannot see the distress his behaviour causes and blames the failure in our relationship on everyone and everything but himself.

In these last three years I have begged for help from my G.P. who has given me sedatives, and from the original hospital who said they could do nothing for him until he asked, and implied that I should take as much as I could and then consider leaving him. We are now in contact with the psychiatric department of a London teaching hospital. After about six months of visits I was reduced at last to tears at the frustration of this brief few minutes from which one hopes that something positive may happen. I was then referred to the P.S.W. and although talking with her has finally relieved the guilt I had felt at wanting to leave him, it is still in practical terms almost impossible, for no one can say what will happen to him. Will he follow me, as I believe, will he crack up or just accept it? Must I and the children uproot ourselves, leave our home and friends and happy school life? If he was normal one could come to some arrangement with him, but with him a promise turns into a threat, and tears into abuse.

This man is as helpless as a baby. But whilst the local authority's health visitor has your baby on her case list the moment you come out of hospital, with help and advice on how to care for it, there seems nothing comparable to help with the infinitely more difficult problem of coping with the mentally sick.

If a man has no insight, how can the professional insist

the patient asks for help and treatment when they must know that he will never recognize his need? Should not the mental health services be as concerned with the future mental health of the families of the mentally sick as they are with the mentally sick and their rights? Is the need less for regression in the mental health services but for a separate system of courts to deal with cases for the mentally sick, staffed by lawyers with psychiatric training? Is it fear of the law or inhumanity which makes the worker in the mental health field say that a patient can only be helped if he asks for help – surely the plea of a relative should carry some weight too?

Cases of premature discharge may be due to lack of knowledge of a particular case, or simply to lack of hospital beds. The tragedy of the above letter shows how urgent it is to establish conditions in which this is no longer the case.

The great problem that faces the mental health services is this: not only do we need planned and co-ordinated services between the community and the new modern hospitals, but also well-trained psychiatrists and psychiatric social workers who can assess family needs on the one hand, the range of available services on the other, and match the two. This is a job for the qualified psychiatric social worker but at present his status only allows him to carry this out under medical supervision, even though the doctor may not have sufficient training in social psychiatry or experience in this field to make the best decision.

It is therefore clearly essential that psychiatrists be trained in the problems of community care. The more they learn about the complexities of psychiatric social case work the more they will value the contribution of professional P.S.W.s, so that both professions will co-operate effectively, both in practice and on questions of policy.

Chapter 5

COMMUNITY CARE

MANY of the facilities for care in the community are available to patients as alternatives to entering hospital; others are intended for those who have been discharged. Some, like out-patient clinics, can be used both by those who have never yet been into hospital and by those who have left after treatment.

OUT-PATIENT CLINICS

Out-patient clinics are extremely important places for preventing and treating mental illness in the community. They are usually attached to general hospitals and are the responsibility of the regional hospital boards. Very often the psychiatrists working in them are attached to the area mental hospitals. This has advantages as well as disadvantages; advantages because if a patient needs temporary or long admission to hospital, the doctors may be able to arrange this at short notice and carry on with his treatment inside the hospital; disadvantages because out-patient clinics have for a long time been considered by the public as the open door to 'asylums', and the very fact that they are staffed by mental hospital personnel may increase a patient's initial anxiety over his future.

These clinics are of the greatest importance for the mental health services carried out by non-medical staff, because they can provide psychiatric and medical cover together with direction and advice. Out-patient clinics have proved themselves to be of value as a follow-up for patients discharged from hospital as well as for those who are living in the community and do not need to be admitted to hospitals. They can advise G.P.s as well as social workers on how to treat particular patients. They have not, however, so far been able to provide much in the way of psychotherapy, being acutely understaffed.

Psychotherapy is time-consuming and may require a very long period of regular contact. The average time available for patients is far too short, perhaps ten to fifteen minutes per week or per fortnight. This is often inadequate and disappointing to the patient, for it does not give him time to relax, to warm up, to focus his thoughts, to explain his feelings coherently, to go into detail, or to mention problems which have been worrying him but which he may feel nervous about mentioning for fear of wasting the doctor's time. Instead he feels hustled and ill at ease, conscious that the doctor is in a hurry, that other patients are waiting outside. In this way, communication is inhibited and important points get overlooked.

> And when I am formulated, sprawling on a pin,
> When I am pinned and wriggling on the wall,
> Then how should I begin
> To spit out all the butt-ends of my days and ways?
> And how should I presume?
>
> T. S. Eliot, 'The Love Song of J. Alfred Prufrock'

Some of these clinics are staffed by the psychiatrists and social workers from nearby mental hospitals. This may lead to confusion. A patient who is under the care of a mental welfare officer or social worker from the local mental health department may find a different social worker dealing with his case at the out-patient clinics. This creates a risk of repetition of functions and overlap which could be avoided if all social workers caring for the mentally ill were under the same umbrella – the local authority mental health service – and had offices inside hospitals. Then the same social worker could see the patient through all the phases of his illness. Such 'joint-user schemes' between local authority and the regional board do exist in some places in England; for example, in York and Croydon. In the latter, the Physician Superintendent of Warlingham Park Hospital, Dr A. May, is also consultant to the mental health service in Croydon. The social workers are appointed jointly to the mental health department and the hospital.

Many patients complain of the little attention that out-patient clinics give. They complain that they have to wait a long time to be seen and that the actual appointment system breaks down because of the pressure of work; they resent waiting several hours to be seen for only a few minutes. This is a general problem of the National Health Service which has been widely discussed in other contexts. Increased staff and a more congenial atmosphere in the waiting-rooms might help to improve the situation, but it will be a long time before the patients' needs are fully met at such clinics.

A number of patients, not normally aggressive, as a result of the long waits approach their doctors with aggression and resentment which has little to do with their illness.

These clinics could also be an important source of help for the relatives, particularly as far as medical matters and medical care are concerned. Yet again, because of the pressure on the doctors' time, very little is done and the main responsibility for this type of work falls on the shoulders of the local authority staff, many of whom are not qualified for it.

It is most important that there should be a link, for the patients' sake, between the psychiatrists of out-patient clinics and the local authority mental health department. In fact, the ideal situation would be if the doctors had a threefold function: to work in the mental hospital, to give some time to out-patient activities, and

to act as consultants to the local authority mental
health service.

DAY HOSPITALS

A further development intended to overcome the problem of institutionalization (see page 70 above) took
place in 1946, when Dr Cameron in Montreal, and
Dr Bierer in London, opened the first day hospitals for
the mentally ill.

They both started with the intention of creating a unit with
less restriction and better morale; a unit where treatment
and remaining in bed would not be synonymous terms; a
unit where patients could stay only during the day, thus
becoming more economical and finally helped to reduce the
demand for full time hospitalization.*

The Marlborough Day Hospital, the first one of its
kind in this country, was organized in such a way that
each patient could belong to a 'firm',

which consists usually of one senior and one junior psychiatrist, one psychologist, one psychiatric social worker, one
social therapist and one or two occupational therapists. A
nurse is added to the team only when the patient requires
physical treatment. Furthermore, it is beneficial if each
psychiatrist either runs or attends regularly one Therapeutic
Social Club. . . . Every patient has the opportunity, therefore, to develop *multiple relationships* with these members of
the staff, groups, and clubs. Apart from these relationships,
most patients also develop a relationship to the hospital as
a whole. This is because the hospital is run as a Therapeutic
Community, and with a meeting taking place every week
which the medical director and all the patients attend.†

* Joshua Bierer, 'Day Hospitals: Further Developments', in
The International Journal of Social Psychiatry, Vol. VII, No. 2, Spring
1961, pp. 148–50.
   † ibid.

By the end of 1964, there were altogether 66 day hospitals in the United Kingdom – 57 in England and Wales, 5 in Scotland, 3 in Northern Ireland, and 1 in the Channel Islands.* During the last two years there has been a further increase in these numbers. This development is of considerable importance because such hospitals can not only continue treatment begun in the mental hospital but, provided close links are kept between these facilities, they can also become a focal point of all local welfare activities.

It is possible that day hospitals will eventually develop within the framework of general hospitals.

When the Mental Health Act of 1959 came into operation there were thirty-five day hospitals or units which offered similar facilities.

They follow no uniform pattern and there is a very variable relationship with geriatric services; some units are purely geriatric, as is the well known Oxford day hospital, some are purely psychiatric, and many are mixed. However, a high proportion of elderly patients has been found to be an unfavourable factor in units treating acute psychiatric illness. Moll divides day hospitals into 5 classes – (1) an integral component of a general hospital; (2) affiliated with a hospital but in a separate building; (3) part of a community service or out-patient department; (4) within the grounds of a mental hospital; (5) a completely separate treatment centre.†

Community care of the mentally ill has to be related to existing services and there must be close cooperation between all these if the patients' problems are to be fully dealt with. The artificial division which exists at present between the local authority service and those services

* *Directory of Adult Psychiatric Outpatient Facilities,* 1964/5, published by the National Association of Mental Health.

† Freeman, op. cit.

provided by the regional hospital board causes unnecessary problems for the patients. Most mental illness can be said to be the result of a disturbed relationship between three factors – body, mind, and environment – which produces inability to function. It is of great importance that the medical and social services which deal with these three factors should not suffer from similar disunity.

AFTER-CARE HOSTELS

After-care hostels can make an important contribution in helping patients adjust to the outside world. Pioneering work of this kind was begun by the Mental After Care Association, which first founded hostels over a century ago and still runs several, mainly in the south of England.

Some patients stay in these hostels for a considerable time and the local authority usually contributes towards the cost of their keep. There is usually a medical advisor to the hostels and superintendents or matrons see to the day-to-day running. Patients can be readmitted to hospital if they have difficulty in settling down.

Apart from the Mental After Care Association's hostels, there are others, usually established by the local authority health service. They vary in size. Some cater for a great many patients; others for only a few.

In January 1960 the Birmingham Public Health Department opened a hostel with room for just twelve men – people who were employable, but who needed help in settling down. The maximum length of stay was specified as nine months and during this time it was anticipated that resident patients would look for work. This hostel consisted of a large house, formerly a nurses' home. A warden and his wife supervise the various activities. Admissions are handled by mental welfare officers and social workers of the public health department in consultation with the doctors at the mental hospitals. Of the ten men admitted originally to the hostel, seven were schizophrenics, two were psychopaths, and one was psychoneurotic. Three of the schizophrenics

got on well at the hostel and left to lead relatively normal lives. Another seemed to be responding well when he had a further acute psychotic breakdown and had to be re-admitted to hospital. The other three schizophrenics showed by their behaviour that they were not yet fit for normal life outside hospital. . . . Little impression was made on the two psychopathic patients during their stay. . . . The psychoneurotic patient showed some degree of stability while at the hostel, which would have been more difficult for him elsewhere, and he later found his own lodgings which proved suitable.*

The authors also point out:

Long-stay patients often improve considerably when they return to a more normal way of life. This improvement is not so obvious in short-stay patients who, when faced with the day-to-day problems of life outside, usually are likely to deteriorate.

The hostel is intended as a supportive and confidence-building place and a testing-ground for difficult patients whose employment prospects are uncertain. The authors feel that such hostels can make a useful though limited contribution towards the care of psychopathic patients.

Middlesex County Council has also undertaken some experiments with new hostels. One of these is Wembley House, an ordinary house in a residential district, where

* W. B. Harbert and F. J. D. Taylor, 'A Psychiatric Hostel for After Care', in *The Lancet*, 19 May 1962, pp. 1064–5.

six women ex-patients live together without any supervision.

The prospective residents of Wembley House are prepared for this temporary communal living before leaving hospital. In a hostel of this kind, where there is no supervision, the residents are responsible for dealing with ordinary domestic problems such as cleaning, buying food, and coping with burst pipes. During the cold winter of 1962, a pipe actually did burst one weekend during the frost. Where many people would have been unable to get a plumber, the residents managed to do so and also dealt most admirably with the mess. A psychiatric social worker who paid weekly visits to the hostel, reported that this event provided a theme for discussion for a long while among the occupants and commented: 'It is interesting to see how, when interest can be focused on external events of this type, patients' individual internal difficulties diminish.'

The residents of Wembley House soon found themselves employment and lived very much as individuals, each doing her own catering and cooking. Occasionally there was a communal meal but this was the exception rather than the rule. Each time anybody who took any special responsibility left, somebody else took over her role.

Patients are not always able to live in such a setting as Wembley House. Occasionally, they may have to return to hospital, usually for a short voluntary stay, but such a return is not considered in any way a failure: no one can be expected to live without difficulty of some sort immediately after leaving hospital. One of the residents expressed what Wembley House meant to her as follows: 'For the first time in my life, I was made to think and take responsibility for myself.'

In addition to its value to its own occupants, Wembley House provides a regular topic of very useful discussion for staff and patients at the hospital, enabling the patients to see a possible future for themselves beyond the hospital walls and helping the staff to keep the community a more open one.

SUPERVISED HOSTELS

Supervised hostels have existed for a long time, but they are still experimental and much practical research remains to be done. It is a moot point whether or not pre- and after-care patients should be mixed (in other words, patients who have not been in hospital and others who may have been in hospital for a long time). And there are also questions as to the advisability of mixing certain categories of patient.

The best way to evaluate such hostels is not by the opinions of the authorities but by listening to the opinions of the patients. Yet I have still to come across any supervised hostel planning committee where the patient's voice is given sufficient hearing. If a number of patients who had lived in these hostels successfully or otherwise were asked to make their own recommendations, it would probably be more useful than collective goodwill, decision, and planning *for* patients by doctors, administrators, and social workers.

The proximity of such hostels to the general community does not necessarily mean that the problem of institutionalization has been eliminated. In fact all that may happen is that one pattern of institutionalization replaces another. If the aim of these hostels is to bring people back into society it is hardly enough that they should be run as external wards of a mental hospital.

One man who stayed in a supervised hostel for a considerable time told me that to break away from the hostel was as difficult, if not more difficult, than to break away from the hospital.

It depends very much on the staff and on the aims of the hostel whether or not they will be beneficial to patients. It seems clear that there is a place for mixed hostels, where men and women patients will live together, meeting during the day, eating together, with arrangements for separate sleeping quarters. In fact such an experimental hostel was opened in Middlesex in 1964.

The greatest thing a hostel can offer a patient is the opportunity for a good relationship with one or more staff members. At first this may be parental in character. The patient may have to learn to become increasingly independent and capable of functioning as an individual. If hostel staff, like some parents, impede this development the patients will remain highly dependent on them. Ways must be found of avoiding this.

SOCIAL CLUBS

Some hospitals, together with local authorities, run social clubs for patients who have been discharged or are about to be discharged. They are an invaluable instrument of social rehabilitation offering patients a chance of a social relationship in which they can be free and frank about their problems without the pretence necessary in their day-to-day life in the community. Such clubs may be a stepping-stone towards other social organizations. Their aim is to offer a social occasion. Tea and biscuits are usually provided by a committee elected by the patients themselves, and there is usually some activity such as table-tennis, darts, or dancing afterwards. Sometimes a committee is elected by both patients and staff. In some clubs there is a small membership fee of threepence or more, but this is not insisted on if the patients cannot afford it. In some of the London (Middlesex) clubs a register of attendance is kept for members to sign. This is divided into 'members' and 'visitors', and staff and patient distinction is ignored.

Most social clubs for the mentally ill are organized by local authorities, hospitals, or volunteers. Their exact number is not known. The National Association for Mental Health has forty local associations, some of which run clubs of this kind. Others are organized by the League of Friends of Mental Hospitals.

At the annual general meeting of the National Association for Mental Health in 1961 Dr Russell Barton talked on this subject.* His address was based on a questionnaire circulated to medical superintendents of psychiatric hospitals and hospitals for mentally subnormal patients and to County Medical Officers of Health:

The 109 replies included reports on 95 social clubs, 31 located in hospitals and 64 located outside. The first club was started by Drs Bierer and Haldane, of Runwell Hospital, twenty years ago. About fifteen have been running for more than ten years. Half the social clubs were started in the last few years.

Miss E. L. Arkinstall, a psychiatric social worker who started such a club, says that the aim is to help people become 'essentially capable'. She feels that the staff should do as little as possible in the way of organization. Sometimes they are not needed at all, but, where they are present, she suggests the following definition of their function:

To use their position as members of the social club, together with their awareness of the special needs of individual members, to act in the best interests of the members of the group as a whole.

* *Mental Health*, National Association of Mental Health, Vol. XX, No. 4, Winter 1961–62.

Such clubs are essentially therapeutic. Simple routine tasks like moving chairs, clearing the tables, or preparing the floor for dancing afford valuable opportunities for cooperation between members. Everyone can contribute something to the group, although often not until they are convinced that they are needed. For instance, if the record player breaks down, one usually discovers a pianist.

Dr A. Kushlick writes:

We see one of the many functions of the club for patients . . . as providing a social framework in which they gain experience and develop their social capabilities. These might have been lost as a direct result of their illness. In addition, they might have been diminished or have failed to develop as a direct result of the long-standing, highly dependent role which they have been forced to play in psychiatric hospitals.*

OCCUPATIONAL WORK CENTRES

One way that has been found to help patients establish themselves independently of the hospital or hostel is the provision of occupational work centres, where newly discharged patients can test out their ability before applying for regular employment.

In 1962 the Blackfriars Settlement started a work centre for some twenty-five to thirty people. Its principal aims were:

(1) To see how far, and in what circumstances, people suffering from physical handicap, mental illness, and old age can be mixed.

(2) To make real work demands on its members and to create a tradition of high output standards. For this

* *A Report on the Mental Health Service of the City of Salford for the year 1961*, by M. W. Susser and A. Kushlick.

purpose they arranged for the making of good-quality, hooked, woollen rugs, designed by well-known painters or by the settlement's own designer, which are displayed at exhibitions and also made to order or sold to some West End stores.

(3) To maximize opportunities for members to play a part in running the work centre. This involvement is allowed to develop at its own speed. At the time of writing, only ten members are actually employed, only two of whom have histories of psychosomatic illness. It is planned that eventually one third of the staff complement should consist of ex-mental patients.

At the moment a full-time organizer and a part-time designer are employed at the Settlement. The Gulbenkian Foundation is financing the scheme's salaries and overheads, but the G.L.C. Health Department has offered to pay ninety per cent of future costs. This occupational work centre keeps very full records so that valuable research should eventually be possible.

Another factory exists in Bristol. In 1960 local industrialists, trade unions, and church leaders founded the Industrial Therapy Organization to help psychiatric patients regain a normal place in the community, and this organization has its own factory employing some 130 patients. In addition to this, a small section of the factory has been set apart as 'a sheltered workshop', and from this was developed the idea of employing patients in open industry, a scheme which has since been put into practice and has received financial support from the Ministry of Labour.

SHELTERED WORK

There is a whole spectrum of facilities for those who need sheltered employment. The discussion of these could itself be the subject matter of a book because they vary from 'occupational treatment' to opportunities for wage-earning work. The Annual Reports of the Ministry of Labour and the National Assistance Board year by year refer to various schemes which they are promoting to meet this need. There are also spasmodic but interesting developments where mentally subnormal men and women are doing full-time work side by side with normal people in open competitive industries. The Annual Report of the Medical Officer of Health of Middlesex County Council for recent years described such developments; and the reports of medical officers of health elsewhere in the country throw interesting light on other somewhat spasmodic but exciting development.

Whilst such work has great value in providing at least a modicum of financial security and satisfaction, it is often of a humdrum character which provides little satisfaction for creative needs. There is a tendency to consider work as an end in itself, but many people in our society can only tolerate their uninteresting humdrum work because they find their outlets and interests elsewhere. Officials and social workers may sometimes consider a case successfully completed when a client returns to work; in fact, if he has no other interests and has not been helped to develop any, he may feel empty, miserable, and depressed, and may easily relapse.

OUT-PATIENT NURSING

To mobilize the resources of trained staff for the purpose of after care, Warlingham Park Hospital in Surrey has introduced mental nurses into the community service.

From a practical viewpoint, the new policy means that extramural care must now be provided for a group of mainly psychotic patients who would previously have been treated in hospital. This group includes convalescent patients discharged from hospital earlier than hitherto, patients who may have relapsed after previous remission, and new patients who are not thought to need in-patient care.*

Most of such a group would normally receive out-patient care and treatment at different hospitals and clinics, or from their family doctors. Psychiatric social workers and mental welfare officers would also be closely involved in the various social problems that might arise.

The authors state that, since 1954, Warlingham Park Hospital has seconded qualified mental nurses to do this extramural work in the borough of Croydon. These 'out-patient nurses' were members of the hospital staff and acted as a bridge between the hospital and the patient.

Because of their nursing training, these people are well fitted to assess the mental state of patients and they often get to know the patients during their hospital stay. Such nurses can 'reassure and encourage patients, supervise the medication prescribed by the doctor, detect deficiencies in personal habits and care and often remedy them, and relieve the anxieties of relatives by timely explanations'. Each nurse is given a number of patients who constitute an extramural 'ward'. There are frequent case discussions under the supervision of the coordinating psychiatrist. Such meetings are also attended by other interested doctors and psychiatric social workers, etc.

The function of the nurse is of course different from that of the P.S.W. Her approach is primarily clinical. Detailed investigation of the patient's family or modification of his environment is not expected. Often nurse,

* A. R. May and S. Moore, 'The Mental Nurse in the Community', in *The Lancet*, 26 January 1963, pp. 213–14.

P.S.W., and M.W.O. (mental welfare officer) may all be helping a single 'problem case'.

THE THERAPEUTIC COMMUNITY

Developments in this field are considerable. A typical example is that of Claybury Hospital.

Over the past eight years, Claybury Hospital has been working out the implications of the therapeutic community concept. The aim has been two-fold; firstly, to reverse, arrest, and prevent the grave personality damage of the institutionalizing process of the old mental hospital system, and, secondly, to incorporate new knowledge from dynamic and social psychology into the overall organization and administration of the hospital. In this way it is thought that a social structure has been created which is in itself therapeutic as well as providing a milieu in which other forms of treatment are likely to be more effective.

The major goal in this development has been a radical modification of the former rigid authoritarian and hierarchical structure of hospital life by opening up communications as widely as possible between all grades of staff, and between staff and patients, drawing the latter as much as possible into active participation in treatment and ward organization. The means to this end has been a network of relatively unstructured meetings in which staff and patients can interact as freely as possible.

As a result of the much freer communication at all staff levels, the real needs of the community can be more fully interpreted by those who have to make and implement administrative decisions. Directly or indirectly all staff play a more conscious and meaningful part in the running of the hospital. Conflict, which is an integral part of any organization involving a number of people, is more open, and therefore able to be resolved, or at least understood. Staff have a greater opportunity to mature and develop their capacity for taking responsibility.

At ward level, the regular ward and staff meetings, which incorporate the principles of group psychotherapy as well as providing the means of free communication, open up greater possibilities of active patient participation and increased use of interpersonal skills in the treatment of a greater number of patients. This approach permits faulty patterns of interpersonal relationships to emerge in a therapeutically orientated and permissive social setting, where they are open to correction and the formation of new and more constructive patterns. An impressive feature of community units is the degree of tolerance and of positive help patients learn to provide for one another, and this is frequently carried on after discharge from hospital.

The major dangers of authority, power, and status in senior staff are greatly lessened in a therapeutic community setting, because these can be constructively challenged on account of the free communication and mutual support of staff members. Lastly, this new type of social structure encourages increase of consciousness rather than repression and provides a sufficiently accepting and supportive setting within which to test out and integrate into the personality new freedoms of the emotional life.*

There is no doubt that, throughout the British Isles, there are remarkable developments in the field of mental health. So far they remain isolated experiments and no national policy has emerged. It can be argued that such a policy cannot be formulated until the successes and failures of the various experiments have

* Information received from D. V. Martin, Claybury Hospital, Essex.

been evaluated. However, there is little doubt that the general situation of after-care services is unnecessarily chaotic and that, without proper coordination, evaluation, and research, it will remain so for a long time to come.

Chapter 6

THE SPECIAL PROBLEMS OF IMMIGRANTS

A DIGRESSION

I WOULD like to make a very brief digression here to mention some of the problems in community care created by immigrants. It is difficult to assess whether or not immigrants are more prone to mental ill health because of the tensions, conflicts, and prejudices set up by living in an alien society, but it is known that it is extremely difficult to help those who do break down unless one has an intimate knowledge of their background, culture, and history.

The reasons why people succumb under stress are varied, but moving to a new country with a very different way of life may be the last straw which completely upsets the balance of a person whose equilibrium has always been precarious. The difficulty of adjusting to a new environment may aggravate latent symptoms or create new ones. Sometimes the new immigrant has a long history of ill health already.

Some of those who came to Britain after the Hungarian Revolution of 1956 were unstable individuals who used the general upheaval to get away. As some of the prisons were thrown open, a proportion of these refugees were in fact criminals and psychopaths. Others were fascists who thought that they were going to carry on in Britain, with their newly gained freedom, where they left off in Nazi Hungary in 1944. Some of the immigrants who were conditioned to a Communist mentality arrived in this country showing alarming psychological symptoms. The newly gained freedom was too difficult to bear after dreaming about it for so long, and too different from the dream, and they appeared to break down with what looked like serious mental illness. However, these symptoms lasted only a few days in some cases and were followed by complete recovery. During this time I worked for a refugee organization and I was often told by hospital psychiatrists that they were extremely puzzled by these dramatic symptoms which, had they occurred in an Englishman, would have required long-term hospitalization. We have yet to learn the subtle interactions between emotional and cultural stability and instability.

Helping immigrants who are ill is difficult because they often find it well-nigh impossible to confide in strangers who do not understand their past or speak their language. It is particularly hard for those who are older, who cling to earlier patterns of behaviour and to old customs and who have never managed to become assimilated.

One old Jew from the East End of London, who had always looked upon intermarriage with one of another faith with horror, considered his daughter to be dead when she married a Gentile. He tore his clothes, went to the Synagogue to say the prayers for the dead, and forbade his wife to mention or see her again. But when a grandchild was born, his wife could not resist visiting her daughter secretly. When the father found out that his wife was in communication with the child he had cast out, a silence developed between them and killed off any love that had existed.

How can a man, who has suffered all the anguish of denying his child's existence because she married outside the faith, then confide in a non-Jew? However well-trained a non-Jewish psychiatrist may be, however well-intentioned, can he really understand the cultural implications of such a tragedy? Can he really help such a family? Many gentile social workers and psychiatrists, who work closely with such people and who understand their traditions and their religion, feel that it is extremely difficult to overcome cultural barriers of this kind. Similar problems occur when dealing with other minority groups, whether the difference is one of religion, culture, or colour.

Adjustment to a new society is a slow process and some members of a family may find it easier than others. If older members cling to the past and the younger ones assimilate very quickly, a family itself may be torn apart, which increases the likelihood of mental instability occurring.

Linguistic shortcomings, a previous background of persecution, lack of a wide family network or many friends, a feeling of insecurity and loneliness, perhaps a very slender attachment to the new social and cultural milieu, all create problems which increase the chances of mental breakdown and add to the difficulties of rehabilitation. Community care under these conditions is made increasingly difficult, for the individual may feel he does not belong to the new community, he may even resent its help, or he may be facing genuine hostility and prejudice from local inhabitants.

Chapter 7

THE HENDON EXPERIMENT

I FIRST came into contact with the mentally ill when I was in various concentration camps, and I would like to show how my own experiences have coloured my ideas, attitudes, and approach to the care of the mentally ill and the problems of 'work-shy' people.

Psychoanalytical literature speaks a great deal about the 'child being father to the man'. It holds that a good, positive relationship with mother (and with father too, of course) gives us strength to conquer, to love and to be loved, and remains a source of strength to us all our lives. But what about those whose early relationships were damaged, who were denied the love which was their right? Are they now damned until the end of their days, only hoping for a better life in the 'kingdom of heaven'? Are early injuries really fatal? Is what happens in the past irredeemable? I do not think so.

During the summer of 1944 I found myself in a German concentration camp: Tröglitz, in Thuringia. I was twenty-one years old at that time and had no training in social work or psychiatry. With hundreds of other prisoners, mainly Hungarian Jews, I found myself on a 'planet' where the laws and rules of civilized life were turned upside down by the National Socialists, and where the ultimate aim was our destruction in the gas chambers. On 16 August the Allies appeared over Tröglitz, bombed the synthetic petrol factory where we prisoners were working, and managed to destroy it completely. After that there was nothing else for us to do but to clear away the rubbish. But one day the commandant of the camp decided, on the advice of S.S. 'medical experts', to do an 'experiment in mental health'. He ordered a few hundred of us to move sand from one end of the factory to another, and when we had completed this task we were ordered to move it back to the original place. At first we thought that our guards must have made a mistake, but it soon became clear that they had not. From then on, day after day, week after week, we had to carry the sand to and fro, until gradually people's minds began to give way. Even those who had been working steadily in the factory before it was bombed were affected, for the work had some use and purpose, even if it was for the Germans, but in the face of a completely meaningless task people started to lose their sanity. Some went berserk and tried to run away, only to be shot by the guards; others ran against the electrified wire fence and burnt themselves to death. Young greenhorn though I was, I could not help noticing that the first people to be affected in this way were those who back at home had always done a useful satisfying job in life – doctors, lawyers, electricians, mechanics, and so on. Those who survived the longest were people used to rather dull, routine, unskilled work at home. The suicide rate in Tröglitz went up and up as a result of this 'mental health' experiment. One day at *Appelplatz* (roll-call) the camp commandant 'jokingly' said 'now there is no more need to use the crematoria'. It was clear that meaningless tasks and pointless work destroyed people.

My comrades had died not at the hands of the Gestapo, but because they had nothing to live for and had been forced to do futile acts which killed their spirit. Society had denied them life and they had regressed into childhood, where their early fantasies about denial were reinforced. If purposeless tasks can destroy people's will to survive, what could purposeful tasks do for them, even for those to whom early satisfactions had been denied? In other words, can the mentally ill be helped by being given a purpose in life, by being encouraged to find some new satisfaction in a meaningful task?

Let Dr Bruno Bettelheim, a psychoanalyst and fellow prisoner in another camp, speak on this subject:

... But my central problem was not whether or not psychoanalysis could explain things, but whether and how these explanations could help me and others to survive as human beings under extreme conditions. Experience with both analysed and unanalysed persons in the camps was convincing demonstration that when the chips were down, it was utterly unimportant why a person acted the way he did; the only thing that counted was how he acted. ... Only dimly at first, but with ever greater clarity, did I also come to see that soon how a man acts can alter what he is. Those who stood up well in the camps became better men, those who acted badly soon became bad men; and this, or at least so it seemed, independent of their past life history and their former personality make-up, or at least those aspects of personality that seemed significant in psychoanalytic thinking. ...*

While in Tröglitz, one fellow prisoner, Dr Ekstein from Prague, put the following to me:

What do you think determines the destiny of a person? What does it depend on, whether one is dragged down by suffering, or raised to a higher level by it? What decides our fundamental sensitivity or insensibility? Biochemists attribute it all to the hormones; psychologists to early and unresolved conflicts; sociologists put everything down to poverty and unsatisfactory working conditions. Have a look round. How many of these people did you know back home? Quite a number. Of the good ones, how many have remained good? And how many of them who used to be bad have become human beings here? The concentration camps have created a civilization within a civilization. And in this

* *The Informed Heart*, by Bruno Bettelheim, Thames and Hudson, pp. 10–17.

new civilization the truths and laws whose validity we believed in for centuries have been turned upside down. . . .
If you compare these two 'civilizations', don't you find
yourself compelled to conclude that the people who under
these abnormal circumstances manage to prove themselves
human are not necessarily those who can do so outside the
prison bars? And if you can see an answer to this problem,
tell me: on what does it depend whether a man remains a
man?*

Across the gulf of over twenty years, I believe I can
now answer my dead comrade: Man is the product of
both the past and the present; the two interact in a
way that is measurable. Not only does the past affect
our todays, but our todays may affect our yesterdays.
Time is only perceived by us in terms of consciousness,
but in the world of the unconscious there is no time. In
my dreams I can look into my own cradle; if I faint, I
may not know if I was unconscious for a day, for a
week, or for a month. In the subterranean life of the
mind there is no demarcation line between the present
and the past, the past and the present. Our memories
are perceived in terms of time because of our conscious
state of mind, but beyond consciousness lives the
eternal, timeless underworld.

This, then, is the theoretical basis I took for my social
research work: Man is not only what he was but also
what he does, and what he is. If Man can be made free
from the bondage of his past to utilize the 'here and
now' by gaining satisfactions from the present, he
may heal his wounds to varying degrees. The scar will
remain, but increased satisfactions in the present will
infiltrate into the unconscious where painful and happy
memories dance together in a kind of subterranean
union. Man may not be entirely free because he is Man,
but he can at least be freed to be truly a man.

* *Night of the Mist*, by Eugene Heimler, Bodley Head, p. 128.

However happy a childhood may have been, society will decide the destiny. Those who killed others in the camps, or who killed themselves, could not find purpose or satisfaction in society; but those who found some purpose in brotherhood, in comradeship, in philosophy, or religion remained human beings and conquered their past injuries. Dr Ekstein's question may be answered thus: a man can remain a man if he has a feeling of purpose which gives him satisfaction in some area of his life.

In 1954 it occurred to me that some of those who live on National Assistance because they are unemployed might be brought back to work through the combined efforts of their families, of society, and of psychiatric social workers. I arranged to work experimentally with forty-one long-term unemployed people specially referred to me by the Hendon National Assistance Board. This experiment not only showed that the value of psychiatric community care could be demonstrated and measured; it was also an attempt to influence social policy. I have already explained how I came to have the ideas which lay behind my research, so I will now go on to describe the experiment in detail.

Hendon is a borough of Middlesex in the north-west of London, with a population of 150,000. Faced with the unemployed there, I thought of those who had survived the concentration camps by finding some purpose for living, and I tried to see if it was possible to apply the same insights to the 'work-shy' of Hendon.

After a thorough discussion with the manager of the National Assistance Board and his staff, I received on referral forty-one applicants and subsequently visited them in their homes or saw them in my office. All the people I saw had been unemployed for at least two years and some of them had not worked for many more. They came from various social groups. Apart from the length of unemployment there was also another consideration. The officers of the N.A.B. had sensed or noticed that all these people had serious emotional problems. This showed itself either by disturbed family relationships or an inability to get on with others outside the family.

When I received a referral note from the N.A.B., I usually obtained the consent of my patient to get in touch with his family doctor, partly to obtain his agreement and support for the work I was doing, and partly to exclude the possibility of treating organic conditions by psychosocial methods.

After intensive work for six months, during which I saw these people once or twice a week, certain interesting patterns seemed to emerge. I found, for example, that the beginning of unemployment in many instances was connected with some kind of marital trouble which had continued unsolved. In order to help such people to return to work one therefore had to assist them with these problems.

It was also interesting to notice that the onset of long-term unemployment was often coupled with colds and 'flu' and many other forms of minor ailments. Sometimes the patients had stayed away from work for a few weeks because of these physical illnesses and during this time had discovered that their wives were much more affectionate when they were ill. Because of this, even after recovery, they had wanted to extend this new-found emotional relationship and so unconsciously created a long neurotic extension to an original physical illness.

Others had lost their jobs through no fault of their own. It was here that I noticed how strongly sexual functioning and social functioning were connected. A man, for example, with an uninterrupted work record since he left school, lost his job because the firm closed down, and, consequently, as a reaction to this unpleasant situation, he developed severe anxiety symptoms. At this point of anxiety he became so preoccupied about his future that he lost interest in sex. His wife, on the other hand, seeing her husband in this disturbed state, wished to console him, and her own love and sexual desires increased. Eventually, he found himself impotent. This increased his anxiety and made him angry with himself and also with his wife. She, not understanding what had gone wrong, was concerned about his attitude. As she put it, 'When I thought he needed me most, he kicked me aside.'

Because of the combination of social, emotional, and sexual factors, this man was quite unable to concentrate on getting another job. He tried to win back his wife, but did not succeed. By the time his unemployment became chronic his sexual desire had increased, while his wife's seemed to have faded again. Not being able to talk it over, he now took to drink.

It wasn't until all these patterns had been brought into the open that one could unravel the past and so try to explain what had happened to these two people, who basically still loved one another. The relationship between husband and wife then improved, and he was able to find another job within a few weeks.

Another group of chronically unemployed are those whose work is not suited to them intellectually. There are, unfortunately, many people in our midst – particularly in the middle age groups – who were unable to qualify for professions when young, in spite of adequate intelligence, because of the lack of educational facilities. These people may withdraw from social life because they feel they could have done better. Fortunately, even at a late stage in their life it is sometimes possible to improve the situation by part-time study.

My forty-one cases of unemployment hid a number

of complicated personal problems and I found that it was possible to identify four main groups:

(i) People who were unemployed because of deep-rooted emotional problems and who, until these problems were looked into, were unable to utilize their energies in work. Dissatisfaction due to inner fears and anxieties was rationalized as being due to the nature of their employment, and they kept on hoping for some fantasied ideal job, or, for fear of failure, gave up looking for work altogether.

(ii) People who, through circumstances beyond their control, had to do unsuitable work in which they could not utilize either their intellectual or emotional capacities. Their work problems were real, and their discontent and constant change of jobs did not necessarily indicate emotional immaturity. Long-term unemployment, in many cases, led to difficulties in their relationship with wife and children. These had to be sorted out before a more suitable form of employment could be found.

(iii) Increasing numbers of people who found themselves without a job because of modernization of industries and automation. Younger people, below the age of forty may, with help, receive some retraining, but those above this age find it difficult to do so. Loss of status and anxiety over the future soon create difficult marital and interpersonal problems and a withdrawal from reality takes place. These emotional problems have to be brought into the open and *the whole family* needs help. Employment then, with guidance, becomes possible.

(iv) A small fraction (less than one per cent of my sample) of people on National Assistance had no incentive to work. Sometimes their benefits added up to more than if they had been out working. These people did not seem to have any particular emotional or social problems and were in the true sense 'work-shy'. Usually they were unskilled people; they found no challenge in working and they were on the whole more satisfied with life when not doing so. To rehabilitate them was extremely difficult.

Through these forty-one cases I also learnt to understand that these patients presented quite a different facet of themselves to me from that which they showed to an N.A.B. officer, particularly if interviewed at the N.A.B. office. The applicant might be demanding and aggressive at eleven o'clock in the morning with an officer, and a few hours later he might be quiet (perhaps too quiet) in my office with me.

There are many reasons for this, partly psychological, partly social. Psychological, because an adult, faced with the kind of problem I have just described, feels like a child when he stands in front of the officer; and because he feels so incompetent and even impotent, he resents the officer's authority and often tries to assert himself by arguing. My role, however, is different. Since I have no power over him, I remind him less of his dependence. Thus his *expectations* of the officer and of me are largely conditioned by our different social roles.

Not so very long ago, public assistance was regarded as charity and this attitude lingers on. People dislike accepting charity which they regard as 'something for nothing'. These people may have paid their insurance contributions when they had work and paid their taxes, but now that they are unhappy and desperate they feel once more like helpless children, but confronted with a parent who – they think – asks what *right* they have to be fed. The officer also represents the Almighty, who may grant favours or deny them. Even some of the prophets of Israel became angry with the Almighty when favours were not granted! The applicant feels as if the officer can supply as much money as he likes and is being mean and bloody-minded when he argues over pennies and shillings. 'The money is all there somewhere in his desk, but he doesn't want to give you much because he doesn't like people who don't work. You can tell he doesn't like you at all.'

One man put it like this:

'You go there, see. They keep you hanging about, while they drink their bloody tea, see. They hate your guts. You can see that by the way they talk to you. You are nothing to them, see? But they fancy themselves like the blooming Almighty. You go to them like a kid for pocket money.'

The arrangement of some of the offices, where everything can be overheard, does not help. There is no way of knowing who may be overhearing the sorry tale of folly and failure, who may be learning the details of his humiliation. Some applicants take advantage of the situation by provoking others to hostility.

My position is very different. I go to the applicant's home, and only see him in my office if he prefers to come there for any reason. I have no waiting crowds. I have more time. The applicant is alone with me and there is no audience to perform to. I don't give money. I attend to his other needs.

Social conditioning has made applicants assume that the National Assistance Board's officers will not be interested in them as people, but merely in their financial inadequacy. Since applicants refrained from discussing 'private' matters and personal feelings with officers for fear of a trap, but were willing to tell their innermost feelings to general practitioners and social workers, considerable misunderstanding occurred whenever the three groups tried to communicate about an applicant.

I started working in Hendon in 1954. Within three to six months twenty out of forty-one patients returned to work, and they were followed up at six-monthly intervals until the early summer of 1961 when they were still working. This shows that cooperation between the Board and the community care services of local authorities can help socially or mentally ill people who are drawing National Assistance to regain their position in society. In this experiment £1,600 was saved, and had it been carried out on a national scale, i.e. had every local office had the benefit of a similar service for forty cases, the total saving would have been £600,000 per annum. (This was over ten years ago; at present rates the savings would be correspondingly greater.) Forty cases in one Board office represents considerably less than one per cent of the total load, and it was estimated that between seven and fifteen per cent of all National Assistance Board applicants could be helped by such a service.

After 1955 the work steadily developed until by the end of 1956 the total number of referrals was 301. Out of these, 82 were referred by the National Assistance Board, 94 by general practitioners and medical specialists, and the rest from various sources, such as mental hospitals, out-patient clinics, and voluntary agencies, while a few were self-referred. Approximately half of the total number came into the category of prevention; in other words, they had never received treatment in a mental hospital or consulted a psychiatrist.

It was soon clear that the most important contribution community care could make was in the field of prevention.

In the Hendon Experiment certain techniques were developed for the rehabilitation of the mentally ill or emotionally disturbed to work in the community. These techniques evolved as time went on and were somewhat different from those of clinics and hospitals. How different can be seen from the following comparison of approaches.

Freud and his followers demonstrated, through psychoanalysis, the great influence of the past on the present. They have clearly shown how past experiences may influence adult behaviour. Through the technique of psychoanalysis the analyst assists the patient to recall his painfully repressed and forgotten past experiences. Thus, the patient is enabled to face his fantasies and reality and is better able to live his life in the present because of the insight, awareness, and understanding that he has gained about himself. The analyst, by keeping his own personality in the background during the process of treatment, comes to represent people in the patient's past life. In short, the patient will feel and behave to him as if he were his mother or father. In psychological language this is called transference. The patient will love and hate the analyst, not for his own sake, but because he is displacing these feelings from his parents. The analyst is able to use this relationship to show the patient how he distorts reality in the magic of earlier experience, and thus help him to distinguish between it and fantasy.

In community care, while the use of relationship is still of the utmost importance, the process is of necessity very different from that of analysis.

In community care the present plays an extremely important part. The psychiatric social worker tries to enable his patient to function better in his present life and uses the present as a therapeutic tool. If the patient can be induced to adopt a new pattern of functioning, this assists him to *feel* different about his past. For in the dark world of the unconscious there is no such thing as time, and although the past cannot be changed, memories can become more complete and more accurate. The feeling about them may be greatly modified by a greater security in the present. *Man, therefore, is not only the product of what he was but also of what he does.* Frustration reinforces past patterns of frustration. Satisfaction can alleviate past frustrations. In short, the theory of psychiatric community care is this: the past influences the present, but the present also influences the past.

In the traditional psychiatric settings the work of psychiatrists and psychiatric social workers is based largely on the patient's verbal communication. The patient tells the therapist about his or her problems and the therapist aims to increase the patient's awareness, insight, and understanding by verbal interpretations and explanations. He tries to bring into the open repressed or rejected material from the patient's past life that is usually painful and which he does not want to face.

In community care these techniques have to be modified. It was soon learnt that there are many people who have great difficulty in verbal communication. There are, for example, many people whose intelligence is limited, or who are very inarticulate. Others are unable to accept the impersonality of the formal interview, and unless they receive help in an informal, quasi-social way, may refuse it until they finally break down.

I remember the first time I realized how much I could use *actions* in the present as a lever for communication and interpretation. Then, with some of my patients I moved out of my office setting and from their homes, into ordinary environments of life where such actions were more easily discernible. I had an interview in a public bar with a man who had great difficulty in telling me about himself in the office but who warmed up over a pint of beer. I noticed that he drank his beer very quickly and put his hand around the glass as if he wanted to make sure that nobody would take it. I remarked on this and said to him, 'It seems to me you are afraid that people will pinch your beer?' He smiled but answered immediately that given half a chance people would indeed take away things from him. Without any further prompting he told me about the orphanage where he was brought up; how the children used to take away his things, and how one day even his shoelaces disappeared; how lonely he felt and how careful he had to be in trying to preserve what was his. I looked around the pub and commented that there were no children about. He could then see how he had brought the past into the present, into a situation where it was highly unlikely that anyone would want his beer.

Another time, a young musician came to see me who suffered, among other things, from claustrophobia, which made it painful for him to sit in closed spaces. He used to play in an orchestra, but he gave it up mainly because of his inability to sit inside the hall. At the time when I met him he was washing dishes in a restaurant and was extremely unhappy. He lived in a small room near a railway station and spent half of the night outside watching the trains come and go. He had been to a psychiatrist but did not return for treatment because the psychiatrist was not willing to interview him in the garden.

We went out to Hyde Park and as soon as we left the office he opened up. In the park he chose to sit in an isolated spot. Instead of delving into his past or into his symptoms I remarked on his *action*. 'You seem to have chosen a spot where you can see others, but can't be seen yourself?' Then he poured out his feelings about himself; how he was frightened of people, and how they could read his thoughts, which were not pretty. He looked at some girls who were sitting on the grass and jokingly said to me, 'They all lead you up the garden path.' Soon he was telling me about his mother, who he thought only cared for him because of his musical gifts. She couldn't show any emotion and gave him little love. I showed him the connexion between his feelings about his mother and about the girls. I think he was able to see how he was carrying the patterns from the past into the present in Hyde Park. He brought his feelings for his mother to these girls 'leading him up the garden path'.

He was an ambitious young man and very soon told me about his wish to become a conductor and how he did not dare to take the final plunge because if he failed his mother would not love him; so he chose failure and his fear of being shut in as an escape from the fulfilment of his ambitions. He felt shut in because he did not dare to break out. Symbolically his gift, his ambitions, and desires were all locked in himself. His desire to escape from the walls of his inner self expressed itself in his fear of all enclosing walls.

After this interview in the park he went back to his psychiatrist and a few months later he returned to his music.

To use the here-and-now as a way of communication, to observe what the patient does and to relate this to past patterns – to use the outer world to reach the inner one – this is one of the techniques of case work in the community. Thus the interview is almost on a conversational level and it always aims to show the patient some reason for his difficulties in the here-and-now.

The case-worker thus tries not just to find a job, any job, for his patient, but to release in the patient something to enable him to choose his own solution in terms of employment. By changing something in the external or internal environment, the worker enables the patient to live a more normal life, with or without his symptoms.

The Hendon Experiment showed quite clearly that

one has first to be able to release the ability to work. Work itself has a tremendous therapeutic function. It seems that man has got to express himself in life in more than one way. He needs to feel secure, and in our society money is essential to security. He needs to feel that he can express his love, and that his love is returned. This love may be directed towards a girl friend, a wife, or children. In early life it is the relationships with parents and brothers and sisters that matter most. An adult man also needs to express himself sexually, and through the mystery of sexual union he may grow into unity with the opposite sex. He needs friends with whom he can share his innermost thoughts without reservation. He needs acquaintances so that he can feel that he is part of society and, finally, he needs to find equal satisfaction in work, hobbies, and interests.

If some of these satisfactions are blocked he will function at a lower level, and if some of these are released this may affect other areas of functioning.

In order to understand the full significance of work, or for that matter the ability or inability to function in society, we have to reach back to early childhood. First impressions of the world are implanted in our minds through the relationship between mother and child. Not only does our existence depend on this primary relationship but also our security and our first satisfactions from life. The areas of human needs or basic satisfactions are as follows:

(i) Security in relation to basic needs.

(ii) Sensual pleasure through being fed, caressed, and cared for.

(iii) Non-sensual pleasure, i.e. mutual affection.

(iv) The basis of primary relationship – 'I am not alone, someone is with me.'

(v) Primitive play activities, at first directed mainly

towards the mother and later towards toys. It is through play that the child develops many skills, and gains much of his sense of achievement.

As the child grows older the original satisfactions are also found in maturer forms in the outer world, but the ability to find them may depend on the quality of original experience. They now appear as:

(i) Financial (security) satisfaction.

(ii) Sexual satisfaction.

(iii) Satisfaction through family relationship; either, (*a*) with the primary family (for single people still living with their parents and siblings), or, (*b*) with the secondary family (if they now live with wife and children).

(iv) Satisfaction through friendship.

(v) Satisfaction through work and/or interests, and hobbies.

Thus society and all that it can offer becomes, as we have seen, *an extension of mother* and can continue what she started. If she failed too massively in one or more areas, the individual's capacity to find all these satisfactions is likely to be impaired.

In order to exist as a member of society each individual must achieve a minimum level of satisfaction in life. It does not matter where it comes from, whether from work or from money, whether a little from here or a little from there, so long as it adds up to a general feeling of well-being. Once sufficiently satisfied, a person can cope with problems and difficulties as they arise. However, when the satisfaction of a man's basic needs falls below a certain level he finds it increasingly difficult to struggle with his everyday life, with all the pressures and forces of social living. He is likely then to give up working as a first step, or to withdraw into himself in an attempt to lessen the number of his difficulties, which only further aggravates his problem. Conversely, a man who is finding it hard to function in society can be helped by being encouraged to find some new satisfaction, or by strengthening the pleasure or happiness he already finds in any one area of his life.

This was one of the lessons I had learned in my concentration-camp days, when I had seen how a feeling of futility and purposelessness caused people to break down. The longer I worked on my Hendon researches the more fascinated I became with these basic satisfactions, so essential to man's ability to function in society. Gradually I discovered that by sheer practice and experience I could assess a client's areas of satisfaction quite early on in a relationship, and I could usually correctly work out in which areas he was most likely to find new strength and how this might be brought about. As my diagnostic abilities increased I found myself assessing people on a scale of points, and I could even do this helpfully and correctly for other workers' patients after reading their reports and talking to them about their clients.

I then decided to try to make this 'Social Function Scale' into a useful and helpful tool which other people could also use; 1,200 ex-patients and their relatives were interviewed to find out why some were able to function in society and others not. Their answers were tabulated over a long period and, after five years, it appeared that those who could now function in society told the same tale: in one or several areas of their lives some needs were now fulfilled and they 'got more out of life' than before. A great many of them used the actual word 'satisfaction'. From the answers given by those who claimed increased satisfaction from life, and from those who spoke of continued frustrations, the five main areas of satisfaction just mentioned emerged very clearly. These now had to be divided into five subheadings, or questions, to permit of scoring. The questions emerged from the answers of the people who were interviewed. Under 'financial satisfactions', for example, the following questions were asked:

1. Has your income increased during the last two years?
   Yes, 4; Perhaps, 2; No, 0
2. Are you able to save anything?
   Yes, 4; Perhaps, 2; No, 0
3. Do you spend with ease or uneasily?
   Easily, 4; Undecided, 2; Uneasily, 0
4. Are you financially secure?
   Yes, 4; Perhaps, 2; No, 0
5. Do you feel financially secure?
   Yes, 4; Perhaps, 2; No, 0

In order to simplify the scoring system a 4–2–0 score was devised, depending on the answers. Thus in each area the maximum possible score was 20, the minimum 0, and the total maximum was 100.

My colleagues and I in Middlesex County Council's Mental Health Department then proceeded to put the 'Social Function Scale' to a number of people, both patients and non-patients, and we found that:

1. People who were in our care scored on average *less than 60* (based on 180 Social Function Scale (S.F.S.) subjects).
2. Another social work agency dealing with problem families scored on average *less than 60* (based on 115 S.F.S. subjects).
3. A random sample of patients from general practitioners' surgeries, who had consulted them for ordinary ailments, scored on average *above 60* (based on 30 S.F.S. subjects).
4. A random sample of friends and acquaintances

scored an average *above 60* (based on 48 S.F.S. subjects).

5. Patients in mental hospitals (in England and the United States) scored *less than 30* (based on 57 S.F.S. subjects).

Although the 'Social Function Scale' needs further rigid scientific investigation and inquiry, the following tentative conclusions may be drawn from the above survey:

(*a*) People who score a third or less are not part of ordinary society.

(*b*) People who score a half or less are the concern of social workers in the community.

(*c*) People who score more than half in fact function adequately in society.

The Social Function Scale may be used in three different ways:

1. By asking the interviewee to do the score himself.

2. By asking the interviewee twenty-five questions, and scoring the answers supplied.

3. Through ordinary interviews the social worker may collect the information and supply the answers, filling in the form *after* the patient has left.

Experience shows that social workers who have a thorough knowledge of their clients or patients, and who have never heard of the Social Function Scale before, can do the scoring once the scale is put to them. It seems that the 123 social workers, both in this country and in the United States, who on my request supplied answers to the S.F.S. 'on behalf of their clients', scored accurately as to the reality of the patients' problems. The final figures seem to confirm their diagnosis from experience. Lying does not seem to affect the scale, since the idea is to measure attitudes and feelings rather than any objective truth.

With the assistance of a team of research workers, the S.F.S. is to be further investigated and the results published in due course.

The Social Function Scale seems to confirm the theory underlying it, that present satisfactions may have a healing effect on the damage done by past frustrations. It can also measure social movement, since an individual's score can vary over time. Although one can never be certain how much of any change can be attributed to the social worker's efforts, it is at least useful to be able to tell whether changes in the desired direction have occurred.

The scale can also be useful for teaching students and professionals how to assess clients, to find out how ill they are and where their problems are most serious. It can also be used for social prognosis. If a patient is about to be discharged from hospital because he is clinically well, the Social Function Scale can predict whether, apart from the clinical picture, he will be able to function in society at the time of discharge. The test can also be used at an early stage of social or emotional disturbance to assess whether or not the patient should be referred to a specialist, and by such early referral prevent disturbances developing into something more serious. In fact it gives a yardstick by which to measure whether a client should be in hospital, under skilled care, or whether he is progressing well enough to maintain his own position in the community.

To sum up, there have been several results from the Hendon Experiment.

Firstly, it showed that many of the unemployed could, with help, be returned to work. Secondly, it showed that psychiatric community care was measurably effective. Thirdly, in order to help my clients, I evolved new interview techniques, and from my detailed study of their problems I established a definite relation between social normality and satisfaction. On this was built the 'Social Function Scale'. Last, but not least, was the influence it had on policy concerning training and community care elsewhere in the country.

As a result of the Hendon Experiment, Human Relations courses for N.A.B. managers and executive officers have been started at various universities. Seminars were also initiated in 1963–4 for N.A.B. training officers at Hinchley Wood in Surrey. This is the main training centre for all N.A.B. staff, and out of this course emerged a syllabus on human relations which has been adopted for all N.A.B. trainees.*

Thus the 'Experiment' has grown beyond the London area and has gained national significance. Apart from the training courses for N.A.B. officers, similar training courses are now also in progress for Ministry of Labour Disablement Resettlement Officers. In the autumn of 1960 half-day and day release courses were also begun for the staff of health and welfare departments (health visitors, welfare officers, mental welfare officers, wardens of hostels, etc.). The 'Community Care' course runs for three years on a day release basis, and leads to an examination at the end of the third year and the award of a certificate by the university for successful candidates. Many of those who have attended this course are reported by senior officers to have made a substantially better contribution to the work of their departments since.

It seems that an effective community care department must also carry out this kind of educational work. This involves consultation with a number of professionals, such as teachers, health visitors, and midwives, whose work borders on community care. It must also

* For more on this see Chapter 9.

extend to mental health education for the public at large. In addition to all this, there has been a growing awareness of the need to present the problems of community mental health and illness on television, radio, and in the press in order to create a more positive attitude towards the mentally ill among the general community.

Chapter 8

DOCTORS, P.S.W.s, AND THEIR COOPERATION

UNFORTUNATELY, there is as yet very little coordination between the various professional groups in the medical services. The result is that the patient is subject to a bewildering number of people, each with his own title, training, job and function, between whom may lie many gaps and whose services often overlap. This is a serious problem with considerable repercussions. This chapter aims to throw some light on the question of the different roles and responsibilities of doctors and social workers and how they can best work together. Details of the training given to G.P.s, P.S.W.s, and N.A.B. officers can be found in Chapter 9.

DOCTORS AND P.S.W.s

The general practitioner is the focus of community care. It is he who has the overall knowledge of the patient's physical and emotional problem, and it is he who decides whether or not community care is appropriate or whether the patient needs out-patient treatment or admission to hospital. Doctors are themselves very concerned about the inadequate training that they receive in psychiatry (for further discussion of this see Chapter 9).

Dr John Horder* emphasizes that, apart from illness caused by emotional disturbances, doctors have to deal with the anxiety and misery which accompanies organic

* In *The General Practitioner and Mental Health*, World Health Organization, May 1963.

illness, and states that the problem of mental health and mental illness permeates the greater part of the G.P.'s work. Emotional disorders often express themselves in a physical disguise, and it is very important for the doctor to find a technique 'to reach the underlying disturbance in order to deal as far as possible with its cause'. He adds that many countries have only one psychiatrist per million inhabitants, but even in those countries where one may find seventy psychiatrists per million, the importance of the G.P. is obvious.

The Working Party of the Council of the College of General Practitioners reports:

To mis-diagnose organic diseases has long been regarded as a serious error. It is now appreciated that to miss psychological illness is just as bad and may lead to even greater unhappiness.*

This report recognizes the importance of the many allies the G.P. may have in the field of community care, i.e. relatives, friends, employers, medical officers, psychiatric and other social workers, nurses, health visitors, midwives, almoners, occupational therapists, physiotherapists, home helps and citizens' advice bureaux, the clergy, teachers, marriage guidance counsellors, psychiatrists, mental welfare officers, probation officers, statutory and voluntary organizations, etc. The authors recommend that more emphasis be laid on training in normal psychology. They recommend that in future doctors' qualifying examinations there should be more questions on the psychological aspects of medicine, that there should be improved postgraduate training for G.P.s in psychological medicine, and that team work with the ancillary services should be developed.

* 'Psychological Medicine in General Practice', in *British Medical Journal*, Vol. ii, pp. 585–90, September 1958.

Dr Michael Balint sums up the situation as he saw it in 1957:

It is no exaggeration to say that to obtain psychotherapy for an adult under the National Health Service is nearly as difficult as winning the treble chance in a football pool. . . .*

Since this was said a number of developments have taken place. G.P.s have sought orientation courses on their own accord and, in fact, such courses were initiated by Dr Balint at the Tavistock Clinic in London, where they have been held regularly with great success ever since (see page 140 below).

Developments have also taken place within the field of general practice itself. Some G.P.s have used psychiatric social workers as a source of orientation and have welcomed their collaboration in practice, for as Dr Neville Davies pointed out, 'the social worker seemed to be a source of orientation to the doctor'.

Group practices have been established in various parts of the country, like the Manchester University Health Centre at Derbyshire House, where a social worker was attached to a group of G.P.s to explore the possibility of cooperation for the benefit of the patient. Other group practices exist also at Harlow, in Essex, and at the University Unit, Edinburgh, and elsewhere. Such group practices and health centres have shown great promise.

A great deal of research and experiment is needed before a new pattern of mental health work in the community, centred on the doctor, can develop. In the meantime the patient and the doctor need one another. The patient needs the help of his G.P. for his ordinary physical illnesses. As some of these are anxiety-creating, the doctor will have to deal not only with the problems

* Michael Balint, *The Doctor, the Patient and the Illness*, Pitman Medical Publishers, p. 282, 1959.

of physical disorder but also with the underlying anxiety. The G.P. will always have a major responsibility for detecting incipient mental illness. He must know the resources of the community and be willing to seek help from others before things get worse.

It is a great mistake to be over-hasty in admitting someone to hospital, but speed is sometimes essential and it is up to the G.P. to make the decision. It will always be the responsibility of the family doctor to prescribe drugs for patients living at home, and he must also see that the patient does not come to depend too much on them. Some new drugs are a powerful means of combating symptoms of anxiety and depression; if he prescribes them it is up to the doctor to make sure that social workers and others know of the effect they have on the patient. Non-medical people often fail to recognize the underlying depression of a patient who is receiving such drugs and do not realize that without them he might in fact be suicidal. Much as the doctor may rely on social workers and others, they, in turn, are bound to rely on him. At no point can community care be undertaken without the G.P. as an integral part of it.

The willingness of G.P.s to work together with 'outsiders' is variable and may be spasmodic. Some use these services to a great extent but most of them do not. This is not entirely the G.P.'s fault. Community mental health services are still in an embryonic state and there are parts of the country where no skilled case-worker is available as yet.

It is a surprising fact that by the end of 1964 there were only 822 psychiatric social workers in Great Britain and Ireland. Of these, only a minority were working in community care (for further details on their training see Chapter 9). 230 work in hospitals, 81 in departments of child psychiatry, 174 in local authority child guidance clinics, 22 in other child guidance clinics, 17 in schools for maladjusted children and approved schools, 113 in community care mental health services, 21 do medical social work, child care, and probation work, 76 are teaching at universities, polytechnics, and other training centres, 16 are involved in research, 28 work for voluntary social agencies, 10 are employed by the inspectorates of the Home Office, Ministry of Health, and local authorities, and 34 are in other posts.

At the Annual General Meeting of the Association of Psychiatric Social Workers in March 1965 the General Secretary, Miss Margaret Barnes, discussed this situation. She said that in 1954 there had been 407 working members of the Association, 42 per cent of whom worked in the hospital services, 30 per cent in child guidance, 8 per cent in local authority mental health services, and 20 per cent in other social work, administrative, and teaching posts. Ten years later the working membership had more than doubled, but the number in the hospital service had risen by only 60, a decrease in the percentage of the total working membership of 14 per cent. During the same period, child guidance staff had risen by 170 and local authority mental health staff by 83, an increase of 6 per cent of the working membership in each case. Senior administrative, teaching, and social work posts other than in the psychiatric field maintained their position with 22 per cent of the working membership, an increase of 122 posts held.

It will be clear from these figures why in the past the doctor has had to rely to a great extent on the mental welfare officer in cases of emergency admission to hospitals. However, today the rapid developments of modern drugs, the changing public attitude towards mental illness, and the growing availability of community care, all contribute to a new attitude towards urgent admissions.

While in the past the Duly Authorized Officer (now called Mental Welfare Officer) had the final say in admitting patients to mental hospitals, most of this responsibility has, since 1959, been transferred to the medical profession. A number of G.P.s are designated by local authorities as competent to sign compulsory admission forms.

The doctor must be concerned not only for the patient but also for his family. In times of crisis he will have to explain to them the treatment a patient is likely to receive or is already receiving in hospital, and he shares with social workers the responsibility of reducing the pressure on the family as much as possible.

When patients return from hospital to the community, the G.P. will receive a report from the consultant in the hospital and will have to supervise the patient, prescribe his medicine, and keep a watchful eye over his progress. The medical and social aspects of after-care are intricate, and lay people should not bear the onus of deciding whether or not a patient is making satisfactory progress. The doctor has a very great responsibility in this work.

In Britain at present, with its large case-load of mental patients, it must be asked whether G.P.s in single practices are in a position to take on such responsibilities. Can they give the time necessary, not only to assess the needs of their patients but also to advise the community care services of those needs? Mentally ill and disturbed people require a great deal of attention, and since G.P.s are already working under considerable pressure they cannot reasonably fulfil their obligations in this respect unless they are in group practice or in some form of partnership.

COOPERATION

The possibilities of cooperation between G.P.s and social workers in the service of the patient are described by Miss Madge Dongray, a trained social worker who was attached to a group of family doctors at the Manchester University Health Centre (mentioned above). The doctors attached to this Centre served 12,000 patients in a densely populated city area. They had not previously worked with a social worker and at first no one had any idea what sort of cooperation would emerge.

Miss Dongray had been a hospital almoner and had also trained in a child guidance clinic. It was suggested to the doctors that patients presenting social or emotional problems should be referred to her. Miss Dongray found that she could assist the patients in the following ways:

(i) Because of her social work training and experience she was able to use the social services effectively.

(ii) Her previous experience, both as an almoner and child guidance worker, gave her special understanding of the family relationships.

(iii) She was able to undertake long-term case work with families.

During the early months of her appointment the doctors seem to have been rather sceptical of the value of social work. In her own words:

My own feelings were naturally coloured by the anxiety of the work in a new setting, but it seemed to me that I was expected as 'a nice motherly soul' to perform miracles which the psychiatrist had failed to produce; as a 'strong right arm' to the doctor to wrest from the authorities houses for all the ill-housed, jobs for all the unemployed; as an 'expert' to clean up and re-educate problem families of long standing; in short, to relieve the doctor of all those painful situations in which he felt unable to be effective in his own right. Those who complain most loudly that social workers spoon-feed their clients and sap their resources of self-help and initiative sometimes demand just this from workers with whom they come in contact.

Miss Dongray also mentions that a social worker can help the doctor when he is disturbed by a particular problem. She found she was more likely to be used if she was on the spot, when she could be consulted without effort and could assess the situation at once and make an immediate contact with the patient.

Another important contribution was to bring to the doctor a fresh perspective on the patient's family situation and also on such varied problems as housing, care of handicapped children, old people, and malingering patients. In addition to this, her social work training and experience enabled her to supplement the information already obtained by the doctors.

At about the time Miss Dongray undertook her work at Derbyshire House, I also undertook an experiment with a G.P. We decided to study the following groups of patients:

1. The anxious patient with difficulties either at work or at home.

2. Patients presenting mainly somatic symptoms where the G.P. had already taken all reasonable steps to exclude physical illness, and where environmental stress was known or suspected.

3. Patients with an hysterical prolongation of an original physical illness.

4. Suspected psychotics.

5. Psychiatric patients under his supervision.

At the outset we saw the patients together and it became clear that the most important qualification for obtaining a good history of the patient's past life and problems was to be a good listener. From this we were able to arrive at a psychosocial diagnosis, a summary of the patient's potentialities in his environment, taking into account his normal and abnormal mental mechanisms. We made a distinction between clinical and psychosocial diagnosis because we found that it was necessary to take into account the social and cultural strata in which the patient was functioning. We tried to show the patient possible connexions between his symptoms and the environmental factors to which he was reacting. Our treatment, therefore, consisted of attempting to help the patient to recognize the reality of his situation, to understand his reactions and the reasons for them, and to help him find a solution to his problems. Often some change in the environment was planned. Thus we would arrange a home help for a harassed mother and part-time nursery placement for her child while she was undergoing treatment. We often also saw patients' relatives. Some patients improved as a result of a single interview (usually lasting forty-five minutes) while others needed more. A consultant psychiatrist's opinion was invariably sought in cases of psychosis, and his advice was followed.

At the end of one year, over fifty per cent of the patients seen in this way had shown a definite improvement, and the doctor also reported that many of them needed less drugs than before.

We learnt an interesting lesson from seeing the patients together. We found that the patients' emotional reactions to us individually differed to some extent. It was interesting to note how, for example, a particular patient responded to a question put by the doctor or myself. We could see almost from the beginning that there was a revival of early patterns of family relationships where the doctor was placed in the motherly role and I seemed to emerge as a father image. This, in fact, was therapeutic in itself, because through these expressions of his feelings we were able to help the patient understand himself better.

The doctor found that this cooperation was a useful orientation for him in the field of psychosocial medicine, and I, on my side, felt that working with him opened my eyes to the intricacies of the body–mind relationship.

Chapter 9

TRAINING

DOCTORS

G.P.s know that their normal medical training leaves them ill-equipped to appreciate properly the hidden psychological ramifications of a patient's illness. Dr MacCalman pointed out in 1951:

. . . Psychiatric care cannot yet be said to be *readily* available, except for those whose condition demands immediate admission to hospital. . . .

The problem is complicated by the resistance which many patients show to anything 'psychiatric', regarding the out-patient department as the open door to the 'asylum', and any recommendation for psychiatric treatment may provoke hostility and resentment from which the practitioner may retreat.

But Dr Michael Balint suggests that the practitioners may also be resistant:

Conditioned by their training, doctors in general choose first among the proposed illnesses a physical one, because they can understand it better, they have learnt more and so they know more about it, and they can express their findings more easily and more precisely.

Dr Horder gave me the following information about the training of G.P.s.

The undergraduate training of all doctors includes some training in psychiatry; this is compulsory. Postgraduate training is optional at present for general practitioners; this is as true for psychiatry as for any other subject.

There is now a course of normal psychology in the

pre-clinical period at many, but not all, medical schools. Undergraduate medical students receive lectures in psychiatry with clinical demonstrations and most have to attend psychiatric out-patients. Some attend ward rounds and a few do a period of 'clinical clerking', following their own cases for one to three months. Most of this teaching is done in the fifth and sixth year, but in some schools, such as Sheffield, teaching is more evenly spread over the whole clinical curriculum. In most schools psychiatry is still treated as a 'special subject' comparable with ophthalmology. The trend for the future is to introduce psychiatric aspects of disease into most parts of the curriculum, some of it being taught by non-psychiatrists. (It is interesting to note that in one Israeli university psychiatry is regarded as the most important subject after general medicine, surgery, and paediatrics.)

In England, there are great variations in the total hours of teaching – fourteen hours in one school, ninety-five in another, the average being about forty-five. In general, London medical schools give less training in psychiatry than provincial ones.

It will never be possible in the undergraduate curriculum to do more than teach basic principles and demonstrate the commonest problems. Increasing efforts have been made in the last twenty years to stimulate the interest of students in this difficult subject and to encourage the tolerant attitudes which are so essential in the care of these patients.

It is still possible for doctors to become general practitioners without any postgraduate training after the compulsory graduate (pre-registration) year in hospital. Most doctors gain more experience than this in hospital posts, and about half those entering general practice become trainee assistants for one year with an established practitioner.

There are a small number of junior training posts in psychiatric hospitals. Formal postgraduate training in psychiatry is available but is taken by few at present. Most of a general practitioner's psychiatric skill is obtained by practical – sometimes bitter – experience. Courses are available in many centres but less than a quarter of general practitioners attend them. Most of them are short didactic courses, but there have been long courses for the last thirteen years in London – the Tavistock seminars, which take place weekly for two to three years. A total of about 220 general practitioners have taken these since 1952. Similar seminars are also available in six other centres in the provinces.

Some general practitioners act as clinical assistants in psychiatric hospitals.

There remain several other less formal but important ways of learning:

(i) Lectures at medical societies, which are very numerous.

(ii) Tape-recorded lectures circulated to small groups of practitioners in remote areas.

(iii) Reading.

(iv) Domiciliary consultations and telephone discussions with psychiatrists.

(v) Case reports from psychiatric consultants.

PSYCHIATRIC SOCIAL WORK

Training for psychiatric social work was originally provided only through specialized university courses of one academic year in duration, which offered concurrent theoretical and practical training. An important feature of such courses is the necessity for two fieldwork placements, one in a child guidance clinic and the other in a mental hospital or psychiatric unit caring for adult patients; as in all social work training, the student works with clients in these settings under close supervision from a qualified and experienced worker. Each university planning to set up such a course therefore has to find within a reasonable distance training centres of both kinds, with a supervisor of the required quality and such other conditions for student training as a full psychiatric team. It is largely these problems which have prevented more rapid development of psychiatric social work training.

Such training was at first provided only by the London School of Economics, followed later by the Universities of Edinburgh, Manchester and Liverpool. A similar course has recently been opened at the University of Leeds. Since the last war there has been a trend towards joint (or 'generic') training of caseworkers who will eventually work in various branches of social work. Courses of this type at Belfast, St Andrews and Birmingham are now able to offer the necessary two psychiatric placements within the academic year, while three more (Newcastle, Southampton and South Wales) offer a second psychiatric placement for a further four months after completion of the basic course. New courses are now being prepared and obtaining recognition so rapidly that this list will soon be out of date.

Students accepted for this training are required to have a Degree or Diploma in Social Studies, supplemented by experience in some branch of social work. Students admitted to specialized training courses have often trained previously for some other branch of social work and practised in it for some years. A number of other students obtain the necessary previous experience through a trainee scheme organized by the Association of Psychiatric Social Workers which enables selected trainees to work (on salary) in psychiatric settings under the supervision of experienced P.S.W.s for one or two years before taking a university course.

N.A.B. OFFICERS AND HUMAN RELATIONS COURSES

As described earlier, on p. 128, one of the results of the Hendon Experiment was a new look at training methods, particularly for those who come across the mentally ill in the community without having been trained for this aspect of their work. The National Assistance Board office staff and I arrived independently and simultaneously at the conclusion that what was probably required was a part-time training course which would convey some theoretical knowledge about human relations, particularly about family interaction, and would relate it to the practical day-to-day work of Board's officers.

Accordingly arrangements were made early in 1958 with London University Extra-mural department, to provide an evening course in human relations exclusively for a group of fifteen volunteer executive officers from offices in and around central London. It was restricted to Board staff because of a conviction that if the course was to be any real use, then it had to bite on the cases the officers were dealing with each day and they had to feel free to discuss them in confidence. It was restricted to executive officers as they are responsible for taking decisions.*

The first course began in February 1958 and consisted of lectures and seminars. One of its important aims was not only to impart knowledge about human relations and family behaviour, but also to allow the members to see their own prejudices and reactions to their clients in a new light.

* K. R. Stowe, 'Staff Training in the National Assistance Board: Problems and Policies', in *Public Administration*, Winter issue, 1961.

For example, one day one of the members presented a case of a 'work-shy' man in his fifties who had been unemployed for many years and who suffered from some form of asthma, 'but', the officer added, 'he looked very well to me'. What annoyed this officer was the fact that this man spent the spring and summer months in Britain on national assistance, living in digs, but moved to the South of France to live with his wife, a French citizen, during the autumn and winter. The officer was convinced that the applicant was simply exploiting the indulgence of the State. He was very annoyed about this man and also with me for teaching concepts which seemed to encourage such exploitation.

When his reaction was studied more carefully, there turned out to be a number of ways in which this officer was upset: why, he asked himself, does the applicant come back from France during the spring; and how does he have money to travel to the South of France every year? Although these questions were clearly formulated, the angry officer could not supply the answers in terms of reality, only in terms of his own emotional reactions. The reason, he maintained, for this man spending only half of the year with his wife was obviously because marriage did not suit him and he could put up with her for six months but not for twelve. Furthermore, who wouldn't spend some of his time in the South of France if he knew that on his return he would be kept by the State?

Such emotionally charged reactions very often illustrated to the other members of the Human Relations courses how personal feelings can affect judgement. In this case, they began to ask the officer concerned a number of relevant questions, which he could only answer weeks later when he was able to overcome his prejudice against this applicant and see the reality more clearly. This is what then emerged. The wife received a small disability pension from the French Government because of injuries received during the last war as a member of the Resistance. This income depended on her residence in France. Secondly, she was a cripple who could not undertake journeys; thirdly, she had inherited a small, dilapidated cottage from her parents which, although it happened to be in the South of France, was not on the coast and certainly had no glamour; fourthly, our applicant suffered from a severe chronic asthma and his wife saved up his fares for him to visit her; lastly, she could not keep him all the year round on her small pension, so he had to return to England for part of the year.

Why was the officer unable to find out all this before the group pointed out his emotional involvement to him? As we continued our discussion, it became clear, both to him and to the other members of the group, that he was critical of a man who lived only six months with his wife and six months alone. Why couldn't others do the same? When this came to the surface both the group and the officer found it rather comic. Beyond the joke, however, was the fact of his emotional blind spot which, until brought into the open, made him see his applicant in a completely false light and prevented him from learning the truth.

Human Relations courses aim to give this sort of insight to those who participate in them. Such insight is not limited to the understanding of other people's problems and marriages but also enables one to perceive one's own.

There was a clear pattern: knowledge and discussion led to an awareness of what actually passes in an interview with a member of the public, especially an awkward one, which in turn led to a clearer perception of the officer's own contribution (for good or ill) to the outcome of it. Some of them were even able to say that the greater tolerance of abnormality and awkward behaviour which they now had was of real physical benefit because it lowered the tension and stress of dealing with abnormal people. Their reactions as expressed on paper read, in fact, so much like testimonials for a patent medicine that the scepticism which fills the heart of all administrators was overflowing.*

During the year 1959/60 Bristol, Cardiff, Durham, Exeter, Glasgow and Nottingham Universities started similar 'Human Relations' courses. By 1964 ten more British universities had followed suit. Similar courses are now in operation for Ministry of Labour personnel, local authority staff, etc., and those who have attended them claim that they are more relaxed with their clients or applicants, and that they are able to make a substantially better contribution to their department's work than before. Most members claimed that the course was not only making a contribution in the field of their day-to-day work but also gave them a better understanding of their relationships in their own families.

Prevention is better than care or after-care. If we are to bring up future generations with a better and healthier outlook on life we must be particularly watchful of those periods of life where problems can easily turn into conflict, and conflict into crises. These periods are the pre-school years; entry to school and subsequent transfers during the pre-adolescent and adolescent periods; the preparation for work, marriage, motherhood and fatherhood, bringing up children, and old age. Proper guidance and support at these important stages of life can be provided only if there are adequate numbers of well-trained personnel and the comprehensive services necessary to reach all those in need.

* K. R. Stowe, 'Staff training in the National Assistance Board', in *Public Administration*, Winter issue, 1961.

Chapter 10

CONCLUSION

IT would have been tempting to describe the various experiments and research that I know of that are being carried out in the field of community mental health. Some of these are original attempts to clarify methods, principles and techniques, but all of them are highly personal pieces of work and so far mostly in embryonic form. In this field we still have to develop an acceptable framework which most practitioners can share. My alternative, therefore, is to sum up what I have written so far and then try to project myself as far as possible into the future.

Throughout these pages I have attempted to share with the reader the feelings that accompany mental illness; the thoughts, anxieties and confusions of patients. Amongst these, the feeling of isolation and loneliness, the inability to share, is possibly the most painful. Whether one is young or old, single or a family man, mental illness opens new and previously unknown dimensions in the heart and the mind of all who suffer. In some way it is as if one has landed on another planet where the rules, laws and expectations are turned upside down. All of us need to have an increased awareness of these dimensions when face to face with the mentally ill. The world of the 'patient' and the world of 'sane' people is, however, the same world; there is a no-man's land between sanity and insanity where we all meet. Often we are disinclined to acknowledge this. This denial also means that we are rejecting the mentally sick. The knowledge that 'But for the grace of God, there go I' is, perhaps, the most important contribution that we may offer to ourselves and to those in mental pain.

I have tried to describe casework as a method of care; how much social workers need to be aware that the individual is a member of a family that is affected by him, and whose condition can affect them; how sick families produce sick members, and how often the recovery of one individual may bring about the collapse of another. To achieve change may be a long process and the social worker's canvas may have to be extended to the whole family. This work is carried out through interviews, often in the patient's home or in interviewing rooms and offices, but sometimes in the ordinary situations of life – the street, the pub, parks – where the difficulties of social interaction may manifest themselves more clearly. Whatever we do, wherever we do it, we are trying to help our clients and patients to understand themselves better, to grow, or to live with their problems. There are times, too, when we can use the negative features of their illness so that symptoms may be turned into socially useful assets. Not only the past affects our patients' lives but also the present; if we can help them to find more satisfactions in the 'here and now', this often changes the concepts and the feelings about the past. The interaction of past and present, present and past, may have great influence on the future.

Casework, however, cannot be undertaken without other services, i.e. medical practice, nursing, and the other helping professions. Whoever deals with people must reach out to all those who also help people. This is particularly important in the field of prevention. During the course of life there are periods when we are all exposed to danger. The great changes that are taking place in our society are increasing our vulnerability. In consequence, at the point where we leave school and choose a career, when we consider marriage, when we face the birth of a normal (or abnormal) child, new work or retirement, all these are crisis points with which we may need help. Change is inevitable and depending on one's satisfactions prior to these changes, one may cope or not. Consequently, social workers will in the future have to be much more involved in helping normal people with normal crises. We have so far been greatly involved in dealing with those who have already broken down.

There seems to be an artificial division between community care and hospital care. The reasons are historical but quite frankly, often 'hysterical' too. The hospital, and all those who operate within its walls, belongs to the community. To enter a mental hospital should not be a more traumatic experience than to enter a general hospital. Yet this, so far, is not always the case. The admission of a patient to a mental hospital can add to the traumatic experiences of his illness and in consequence may put an extra cross on to his already weak shoulders. Many hospitals are aware of this and, by a new community approach, may reduce this trauma and the patient's dependence on the hospital. There is a simple philosophy that helps to reduce the dangers of institutionalization: from the moment the patient enters the hospital plans for his discharge must be made. Yet still many people are staying within the hospital walls because they have not been prepared to face the world outside.

Whilst hospitals must plan for the patient's discharge, they also must clarify their minds as to *where* and *when* the patient should go. There are some patients who should not return to their families, whilst others with careful preparation may do so. But in this connexion it is also important that the social workers of the hospital and the community should build real bridges between themselves. Very often cooperation remains, in fact, an empty word.

Outpatient clinics, day hospitals, hostels, social clubs, occupational and work centres, sheltered workshops, domiciliary nursing, are all important aspects of community care. Without such facilities discharge may be meaningless, or bound to fail.

Throughout the years, through trial and error, I have attempted to rehabilitate people. In the Hendon Experiment I carefully recorded how measurable social work was in terms of useful social functioning. Fifty per cent success, however, means fifty per cent failure. It was in this area of failure that I first began to understand the relationship of dissatisfactions and the inability to function in society. It was clear that social functioning, or social normality, was directly related to five basic areas of satisfaction. As the years went by, with the help of my colleagues and research workers, we were able to define, on a points system, social normality. This, in turn, led me to a new field: that of prevention. And it is in this field that I believe the future of our profession lies. Since 1 April 1965, my colleague, Miss Julia Dighton, and I, with the involvement of other social workers, voluntary organizations and the clergy, have begun to explore measurable ways and means through which we could reduce the incidence of social breakdown. This research, called the Hounslow Project, has received the help and encouragement of a far-seeing London borough and now begins to attract the attention of American social workers and universities. It is possible that, with a considerable extension of this work, within three years we shall be able to share our findings more fully with both our colleagues and other professions in this country and abroad. Our work is difficult because for the first time we are trying to measure in a scientific way matters that are difficult to measure. But we have enough knowledge now to say that this work is possible. Once completed, we hope to prove that our profession can contribute something significant in the field of prevention of mental breakdown. And even if we cannot prepare a blueprint for all ills, we may contribute towards the reduction of pain and suffering in our society.

GLOSSARY

After-care homes (see pp. 91–5). These are places of residence for ex-mental patients and represent 'half-way' houses between the hospital and the community. There are several such homes run by the Mental After-Care Association in Southern England, but local authorities now tend to provide their own after-care homes, and there are some other voluntary hostels, i.e. The Richmond Fellowship. The purpose of these is to help ex-patients in the process of rehabilitation. Patients may go out to work from these homes and may stay for long or short periods as the need may be. The homes vary in size and there is a considerable amount of experimentation at present as to which is the best form to suit patients' needs.

Day centres (see pp. 97–9). Local authorities provide such centres for people living at home who are incapacitated for gainful employment on account of emotional difficulties, or for people who return home on discharge from hospitals. These day centres may provide all kinds of organized activities or may cater for individual needs, for example, a secretary who has had a breakdown and has not been able to type for some time and who may be able to recover her skill by practice in sheltered conditions. At the same time she may take part in group discussions organized by the worker in charge of the centre.

Day hospitals (see pp. 89–91) are provided by Regional Hospital Boards and are generally attached to larger hospitals. The patients return home each night.

General Practitioners. For details of the training and work of doctors in general practice see pp. 130–3 and 140–2.

Mental Health Act of 1959. For details of emergency admission to hospital under this Act of Parliament see p. 42.

Mental Welfare Officer (M.W.O.) (see page 135). These are social workers who deal with mentally ill patients in the community. Their function has been described as care and after-care under the Mental Health Act 1959. Before the present Act these workers specialized in admission procedures under the 1891 Lunacy Act, amongst which compulsory admission was important. For these functions formal training was not considered necessary, but now that the role has been reformulated as a mental health social worker, appropriate training courses are being developed in Colleges of Further Education. These Officers are employed by the Health Department of Local Authorities and work under the Medical Officer of Health.

National Assistance Board (*N.A.B.*). A Department set up under the National Assistance Act, 1948, to pay cash allowances to people in Great Britain who are in financial need. It is also required to promote the welfare of the people with whom it is concerned. Any person over the age of 16 who is not in full-time work or involved in a trade dispute is eligible to apply. The Board, consisting of a Chairman, Deputy Chairman, and up to four other members, is appointed by the Crown. Their staff of some 13,000 Civil Servants operate mainly from 430 local offices. The Board is an autonomous body financed by the Central Government from general taxation and not from National Insurance contributions. The Minister of Pensions and National Insurance, although he has no executive control, answers for the Board in Parliament. On 28 November 1966 the National Assistance Board ceased to exist and, *within* the new Ministry of Social Security, a Supplementary Benefits Commission was created. The new Ministry has now combined the function of the former Ministry of Pensions and National Insurance and the National Assistance Board.

National Assistance Board Officers (for training details see p. 144). The National Assistance Board is specially constituted and it is not directly under any Ministry, although indirectly the Minister of Pensions and National Insurance reports to Parliament on its behalf. The Crown nominates its Chairman. The Secretary of the National Assistance Board is responsible to the Board (consisting of seven people) and the Chairman. The Board gives assistance to those in need from a specific National Fund which in Britain is quite separate from Insurance and Unemployment benefits. The Board carries out its policy through Regional and Local Officers throughout Britain and is staffed by Civil Servants. The Board has also under the National Assistance Act 1958 some welfare functions. Anyone over 16 may apply for assistance if he is in financial need.

Psychiatrists are doctors of medicine who, having passed their basic medical degree, have taken a post-graduate diploma in psychological medicine (they have the letters D.P.M. after their name). Psychoanalysis is not a part of their training curriculum.

Psychiatric Social Workers (P.S.W.) (for details of their training see pp. 142–3). These are social workers who have a basic training in social science and hold a degree, diploma or certificate in psychiatric social work. P.S.W.s are registered with the British Association of Psychiatric Social Workers and are entitled to use the letters A.A.P.S.W. after their names. They may work in hospitals or clinics, be attached to local authority health departments, or do research work.

Psycho-analysts. These may or may not have medical training, their qualifications being based on rigorous training, which includes personal psycho-analysis at the Institute of Psycho-analysis (or some comparable body overseas). The word 'psycho-analysis' correctly used refers only to the followers of Freud. There are, however, other schools of psychotherapy such as the followers of Jung, known as analytical psychologists. Nowadays the area of agreement between the various schools is much greater than that of disagreement.

Psychologist. Psychologists are mainly concerned with assessing intelligence and personality. They are *not* Doctors of Medicine but have degrees in psychology followed by clinical training if they intend to work in clinics and hospitals. Psychologists also work outside the health service in industry, education, or in research. Broadly speaking, a psychologist is concerned with the normal functioning of the mind, a psychiatrist with the pathological. Psychologists are not qualified to carry out treatment, unless they have taken further training in psychotherapy.

Psychotherapists. Psychotherapy is a general term for psychological treatment. There are many forms of psychotherapy, of which psycho-analysis is one; other forms may be practised by psychiatrists, general practitioners, non-medicals with special training, child psychotherapists and others. In each case a special training is given which usually consists of several years of postgraduate work at a recognized training institute.

Social clubs (see pp. 95–7). These clubs, sometimes called psychiatric social clubs, are often run by local authorities, with the close co-operation of hospitals. Patients living in the community may attend with their wives or friends, and people discharged from mental hospitals may find an opportunity for social activities and for gaining social confidence and social skills. These clubs have proved to be very useful, particularly in helping lonely people.

Sub-normal people. Those people whose intellectual development is arrested from birth or from an early age and who may also be mentally ill. Services are provided by local authorities for both subnormal children and adults. Social workers arrange foster-care for children where necessary. Training schools exist for children and adults where they are trained in factory and domestic work and encouraged to become as independent as their limitations allow.

INDEX